ELECT
FOR

by

R. A. Penfold

BERNARD BABANI (publishing) LTD
THE GRAMPIANS
SHEPHERDS BUSH ROAD
LONDON W6 7NF
ENGLAND

Please Note

Although every care has been taken with the production of this book to ensure that any projects, designs, modifications and/or programs, etc., contained herewith, operate in a correct and safe manner and also that any components specified are normally available in Great Britain, the Publishers do not accept responsibility in any way for the failure, including fault in design, of any project, design, modification or program to work correctly, or to cause damage to any other equipment that it may be connected to or used in conjunction with, or in respect of any other damage or injury that may be so caused, nor do the Publishers accept responsibility in any way for the failure to obtain specified components.

Notice is also given that if equipment that is still under warranty is modified in any way or used or connected with home-built equipment then that warranty may be void.

First Published - June 1995

British Library Cataloguing in Publication Data

Penfold, R. A.

Electronic Projects for Experimenters

I. Title

621.381

ISBN 0 85934 371 5

Printed and Bound in Great Britain by Cox & Wyman Ltd, Reading

Preface

Electronics is one of those hobbies that different people pursue in different ways. For some the hobby entails building useful electronic gadgets to a very high standard, with many of the completed units having a very professional finish both internally and externally. Others simply like dabbling with components and circuits, and trying out new ideas. The more novel the gadget, the greater its interest value, and the stronger the incentive to build it. The finished units may be archetypal "rats nests" inside and eyesores on the outside, or they may be finished to a high standard. Either way, the appearance of the finished unit is of secondary importance, as is its usefulness. The primary interest is in what the circuit can do, how it does it, and in trying to "fine tune" it.

This book is primarily aimed at the electronics experimenter who would like to try out some unusual designs. I can not claim that the projects are all totally new and that nothing like them has been published in the past. However, I have seen nothing published previously about some of the subjects covered, and the other topics have so far received little attention in the technical press. The circuits provided may or may not have practical applications, but they are all interesting to "play" with. All the designs are tried and tested, but they would probably benefit from further development. There is plenty of scope for those with the necessary technical knowledge to try a few improvements here and there. The subjects covered include linear Hall effect devices, passive infra-red detection, pyro-sensors as breeze detectors, class D amplification, echo sounding, ultrasonic detection, and many more.

R. A. Penfold

Contents

HALL EFFECT DETECTOR

There are various methods of detecting and measuring magnetic fields, and using Hall effect devices is one of the more hi-tech methods. Surprisingly perhaps, this effect was discovered by E. H. Hall as long ago as 1879. Although "off the shelf" Hall effect devices may be relatively new, the effect itself was discovered well over a hundred years ago, and is far from new. An interesting aspect of these devices is that they will respond to a static magnetic field, and unlike some other types of magnetic field sensor they are not reliant on the field constantly changing.

Hall effect devices offer plenty of opportunities for experimentation, but until quite recently they have been quite expensive. Some of these components are still relatively expensive, but there are now a few low cost Hall effect devices which can be bought for about one pound each. At that sort of price they are definitely worth buying for their "play value" if nothing else.

Good Effect

The Hall effect is basically quite straightforward, and Figure 1 helps to explain the way in which a Hall effect sensor works. Figure 1(a) shows the basic scheme of things with no magnetic field applied to the sensor. The sensing element is basically just a slice of silicon having two electrodes placed centrally on opposite faces of the slice. A current is passed through the slice of silicon, giving a potential gradient. The top of the slice is at the full supply voltage, the bottom is at 0 volts, and the electrodes are at half the supply voltage since they are half way up the slice. As the two electrodes are at the same potential, there is no voltage difference across them, and no output potential from the sensor.

Figure 1(b) shows the effect off applying a magnetic field to one side of the silicon slice. The current still flows through the piece of silicon, and also as before a potential gradient is produced. However, the current carriers are deflected, giving a distorted current flow. This is often likened to the electron beam of a cathode ray tube (c.r.t.) being deflected by a magnetic field, but in this case the deflection is much less. Even so, it is sufficient to skew the potential gradient slightly, giving a

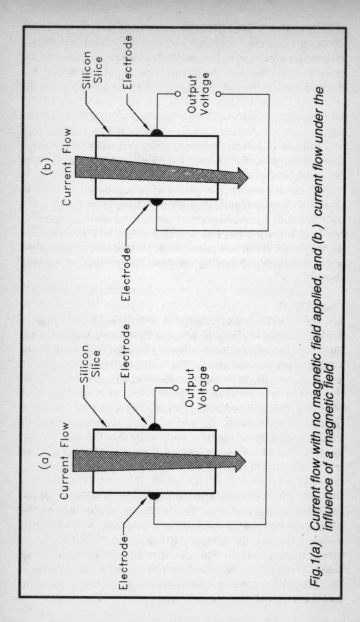

Fig.1(a) Current flow with no magnetic field applied, and (b) current flow under the influence of a magnetic field slightly higher voltage at one electrode, and a slightly reduced potential at the other. This produces a small voltage difference across the electrodes. The stronger the magnetic field, the greater the distortion of the current flow, and the larger the differential output voltage from the sensor. Reversing the polarity of the magnetic field reverses the direction in which the current flow is deflected, and alters the polarity of the output signal.

Practical Hall effect devices are normally more than just the sensing element. There is usually a substantial amount of built-in electronics, which in many cases operates an open collector output transistor when a magnetic field of adequate strength is detected. Switch type Hall effect devices are certainly very useful, and many of these components are quite cheap. The linear type are probably of greater interest to the electronics experimenter though. These consist of a Hall effect sensor plus a d.c. amplifier to boost the output voltage shift for a given field strength.

The 634SS2 linear Hall effect device retains the differential outputs of the basic Hall sensor, but one output terminal can be ignored if only a single output is needed. The LOHET 1, LOHET 2, and UGN3503U are three terminal devices which have just the one output terminal. The UGN3503U is much cheaper than the other devices mentioned here, but it has quite a useful level of performance. Consequently, it is this device that is used as the basis of the circuits featured in this book (but they will probably operate properly using any of the other devices). Pinout details for the UGN3503U are provided in Figure 2. The encapsulation seems to be symmetrical, but the type number provides a means of distinguishing between the notional front and rear surfaces of the device.

Despite the built-in amplification the sensitivity of these components is not particularly high. The sensitivity of the UGN3503U is typically 1.3 millivolts per G. Placing the end of a small bar magnet right against one of these sensors will produce quite a large voltage swing (typically a little under one volt), but at a distance of about 25 millimetres the change in output voltage is very low (about 20mV). Where small magnetic fields must be measured it is necessary to use some external amplification.

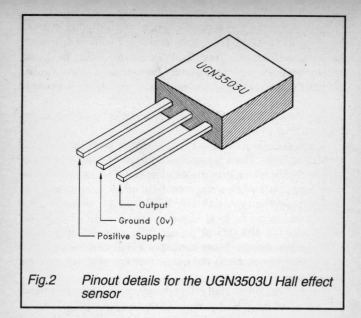

Output

Ground (0v)

Positive Supply

Fig.2 *Pinout details for the UGN3503U Hall effect sensor*

Like any linear Hall effect sensor, the output voltage increases for a magnetic field of one polarity, and decreases for a field of the opposite polarity. Applying a north pole to the surface that carries the type number gives a reduction in the output voltage – applying a south pole to this surface produces an increase in the output voltage (Figure 3). Applying the magnet to the opposite surface of the sensor has the opposite effect (a north pole gives increased output voltage, and a south pole gives decreased output potential). The sensing element would seem to be positioned slightly closer to the surface which carries the type number, effectively making this side of the device slightly more sensitive than the plain one. However, the difference in sensitivity seems to be quite small, and is not usually of any significance.

It is important to realise that the sensor will not respond to a magnetic field applied to one of the four smaller surfaces. A

4

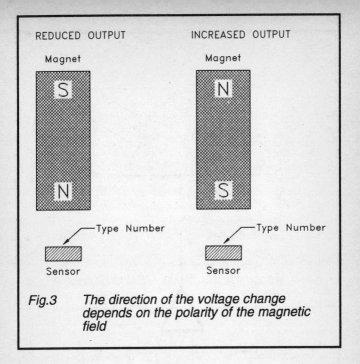

REDUCED OUTPUT | INCREASED OUTPUT

Magnet | Magnet

S | N

N | S

Type Number | Type Number

Sensor | Sensor

Fig.3   The direction of the voltage change depends on the polarity of the magnetic field

magnetic field from any of these directions produces identical voltage changes at the electrodes of the sensing element, and therefore no change in output voltage from the sensor.

The Circuit
Figure 4 shows the circuit diagram for a magnetic field strength meter. Presumably it would be possible to calibrate the unit against a proper gaussmeter, but this is academic for most constructors as they will not have access to such an instrument (or be prepared to pay the typical £500 asking price for one of these instruments!). This circuit is really only intended as a means of making comparative checks of magnetic field strength, and it is not intended to form the basis of a "proper" scientific measuring instrument.

The circuit is very straightforward, and it is basically just the

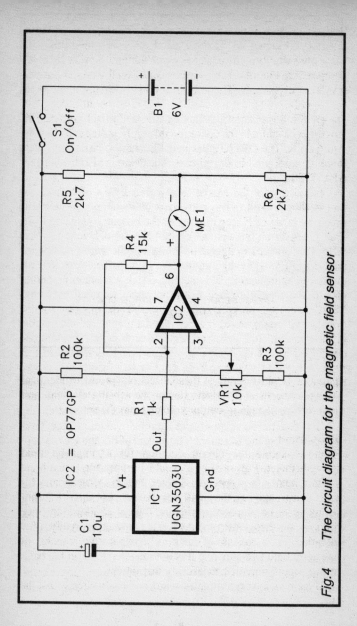

Fig.4 The circuit diagram for the magnetic field sensor

Hall effect sensor, and a d.c. amplifier driving a centre-zero moving coil meter. IC1 is the Hall effect sensor, and this will work on a supply voltage of between 4.5 and 6 volts (8 volts absolute maximum). In this case it is powered from a nominal 6 volt battery supply. The amplifier is an inverting mode type based on IC2. The device used for IC2 must be an instrument grade operational amplifier having low d.c. offset voltages. It must also be suitable for operation at supply voltages as low as 5 to 6 volts. The OP77GP has suitable characteristics and was found to work well in this circuit. The same is also true of the OPA177GP.

R1 and R4 set the closed loop voltage gain of IC2 at 15 times. VR1 is adjusted to provide a bias voltage to the non-inverting input of IC2 that matches the output voltage of IC1. This gives an output voltage of half the supply voltage. The meter is connected in a form of bridge circuit, with one side of the bridge formed by the output stage of IC2. The other side of the bridge is formed by R5 and R6, which provide a potential of half the supply voltage to the negative terminal of meter ME1. This gives no voltage across ME1 under standby conditions, and it therefore reads zero. When a magnetic field results in the output of IC2 going more positive, a positive voltage is developed across the meter, and its pointer is deflected to the right. A negative swing at the output of IC2 results in a negative voltage being produced across the meter, and its pointer then moves to the left. The meter therefore indicates the polarity of the applied magnetic field as well as its relative strength.

ME1 can be an inexpensive "tuning" meter of the type intended for use in FM tuners. The values of R5 and R6 are correct for a meter having a sensitivity of 500-0-500 microamps. For a type having a sensitivity of about 200-0-200 microamps or 250-0-250 microamps the value of R5 and R6 should be increased to 5k6. An ordinary 100-0-100 microamp moving coil panel meter can be used if preferred, but a value of 12k should then be used for R5 and R6. The current consumption of the circuit is approximately 8 milliamps. This gives an extremely long battery life.

This simple circuit is easy to construct, and neither of the integrated circuits are static sensitive types. It is still worthwhile using a holder for IC2 which is not an inexpensive device. With this type of equipment the sensor is normally mounted in a probe which is applied to the source of the magnetic field. The probe should obviously not include any magnetic metal such as steel, and it is probably best to only use plastic in its construction. I used the case of an old plastic pen for the prototype probe. IC1 connects to the main unit via a piece of screened twin cable. The outer braiding carries the "Gnd" connection, and the inner conductors carry the "V+" and "Out" connections. The connecting lead can be a few metres long if necessary, but in normal use a lead about half a metre or so in length will suffice. The four HP7 size batteries are fitted into a plastic holder, and the connections to the holder are made via a standard PP3 style battery clip.

The prototype is reasonably sensitive. A Maplin "large" bar magnet produces full scale deflection of the meter at a range of about 15 millimetres. The magnet can be detected at a range of around 70 millimetres. Virtually any piece of iron or steel seems to be slightly magnetic, and produces a weak field that can be easily detected using this unit.

Components for Magnetic Sensor (Fig. 4)

Resistors (all 0.25 watt 5% carbon film)
R1   1k
R2   100k
R3   100k
R4   15k
R5   2k7 (see text)
R6   2k7 (see text)

Potentiometer
VR1   10k lin

Capacitor
C1   10µ 25V elect

Semiconductors
IC1   UGN3503U
IC2   OP77GP or OPA177GP

Miscellaneous

ME1	500-0-500μA "tuning" meter (see text)
B1	6 volt (4 × HP7 size cells in holder)
S1	SPST min toggle
	8 pin DIL IC holder
	Battery connector
	Case
	Circuit board
	Materials for probe (see text)
	Wire, solder, etc.
	Control knob

HALL EFFECT COMPASS

Linear Hall effect devices can be used to detect extremely weak magnet fields, which begs the question "can they be used to detect the earth's magnetic field?". They can indeed be used to detect a magnetic field as weak as that produced by the earth. If the sensor of the unit described previously is held in a vertical position and slowly rotated, a slight movement from the pointer of ME1 is just about noticeable. In order to produce a really strong deflection of the meter it is necessary to use much higher gain. The actual strength of the earth's magnetic field apparently varies from about 0.25mG to 0.7mG.

Figure 5 shows a suitably modified magnetic sensor circuit, and this is essentially the same as the original circuit (Figure 4). The value of R4 has been greatly increased, and this boosts the closed loop voltage gain of IC2 from 15 times to 1000 times. This level of gain might prove to be excessive in some cases, and the gain should then be reduced somewhat by reducing the value of R4 to 470k. C3 provides a substantial amount of high frequency roll-off, and this helps to avoid problems with excessive noise.

The decoupling provided by C2 at IC2's non-inverting input also helps to keep noise problems at bay. Getting the bias voltage at the non-inverting input set with a suitably high degree of accuracy is quite tricky. Consequently, the normal bias level control (VR2) is augmented by a "fine" adjustment control (VR1). The specified values for R5 and R6 are for a meter having a sensitivity of about 500-0-500μA. For a 250-0250μA or 200-0-200μA meter a value of 10k should be used. For a

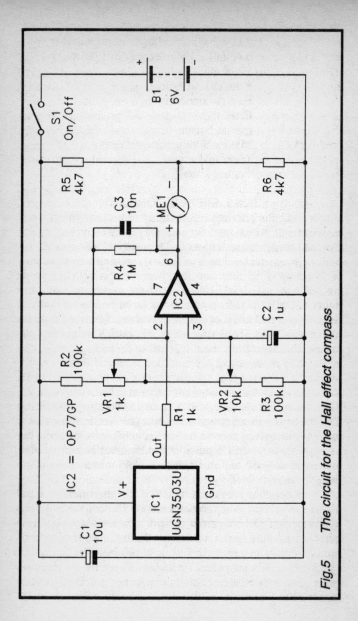

Fig.5   The circuit for the Hall effect compass

100-0-100µA meter R5 and R6 should have a value of 22k.

In use the Hall effect sensor must be in a vertical position (i.e. the leadout wires pointing downwards). Like any form of compass it must be used well clear of any magnets, pieces of steel or iron, or anything that produces even a weak magnetic field. This includes most electronic gadgets. I found that quite a large variation in the meter reading was produced. The reading peaks when the side of the sensor which carries the type number is facing due south (magnetic south that is). Minimum reading from the meter is obtained when this side of the sensor faces due north.

With careful adjustment it is possible to find magnetic north/south with a fair degree of accuracy. It seems to be much easier to obtain accurate results using a medium or large size meter, rather than a small "tuning" type meter. Unfortunately, a "proper" panel meter substantially increases the cost of the unit. The only real problem with the circuit is that it lacks really good stability. There are a number of possible causes, but probably the main one is a lack of really good temperature stability in the Hall effect sensor itself. Stability is quite poor for several seconds after switch-on, and it is worth waiting for things to stabilise before adjusting VR1 and VR2 to bring the meter readings within the full scale values, and adjusting the orientation of the sensor.

Figure 6 shows the circuit diagram for a modified Hall effect compass which has a voltage controlled oscillator (v.c.o.) rather than a meter. It enables good accuracy to be obtained without resorting to an expensive panel meter. This version will probably be preferred by those who have a good sense of pitch, but is probably not worth building if you are literally tone-deaf, or have a weak sense of pitch. IC3 is a CMOS micro-power phase locked loop, but in this circuit only its v.c.o. section is utilised, and no connections are made to any of the other stages. C4 and R6 are the timing components for IC3. The output feeds earphone socket JK1 via series resistor R5. Only a crystal earphone will give good results with this circuit. There is insufficient output from IC3 to drive magnetic earphones or headphones. If loudspeaker operation is preferred, simply replace JK1 with a cased ceramic resonator. In order to obtain good volume it will probably be necessary to reduce the value

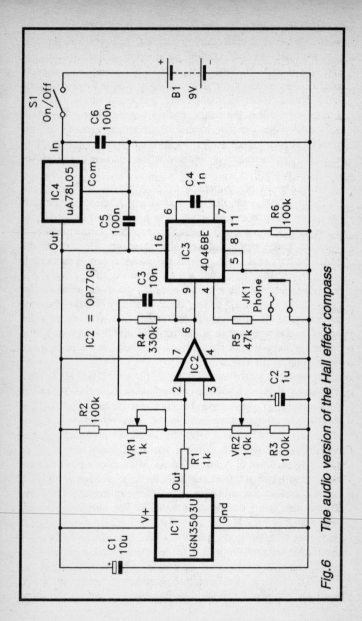

Fig.6   The audio version of the Hall effect compass

12

of R5 to about 6k8.

In order to improve stability this version of the unit is powered from a stabilised 5 volt supply. This is derived from a 9 volt supply via monolithic voltage regulator IC4. The same method can be used to power the metered version of the unit, and should provide a worthwhile improvement in its general stability.

In use it is probably easier to adjust the unit for minimum pitch than maximum pitch. Also, VR1 and VR2 should be adjusted so that the minimum pitch from the unit is quite low, rather than well into the upper audio range. Provided you have a reasonably good sense of pitch it is possible to obtain quite accurate results, but like the metered version, this unit suffers from a lack of really good stability. It is best to wait a short while after switch-on before attempting to take a reading. I do not know if either version of the compass offers a worthwhile alternative to a conventional magnetic needle type, but they are certainly fascinating circuits to play with.

Components for Hall Effect Compass (Fig. 5)

Resistors (all 0.25 watt 5% carbon film)
R1   1k
R2   100k
R3   100k
R4   1M
R5   4k7 (see text)
R6   4k7 (see text)

Potentiometers
VR1   1k lin
VR2   10k lin

Capacitors
C1   10μ 25V elect
C2   1μ 50V elect
C3   10n polyester

Semiconductors
IC1   UGN3503U
IC2   OP77GP or OPA177GP

13

Miscellaneous

ME1	500-0-500µA "tuning" meter (see text)
B1	6 volt (4 × HP7 size cells in holder)
S1	SPST min toggle
	8 pin DIL IC holder
	Battery connector
	Case
	Circuit board
	Wire, solder, etc.
	Control knob

Components for Hall Effect Audio Compass (Fig. 6)

Resistors (all 0.25 watt 5% carbon film)

R1	1k
R2	100k
R3	100k
R4	330k
R5	47k
R6	100k

Potentiometers

VR1	1k lin
VR2	10k lin

Capacitors

C1	10µ 25V elect
C2	1µ 50V elect
C3	10n polyester
C4	1n polystyrene
C5	100n ceramic
C6	100n ceramic

Semiconductors

IC1	UGN3503U
IC2	OP77GP or OPA177GP
IC3	4046BE
IC4	µA78L05 (100mA 5V positive reg.)

Miscellaneous
B1   9 volt (6 × HP7 size cells in holder)
S1   SPST min toggle
            8 pin DIL IC holder
            16 pin DIL IC holder
            Battery connector
            Case
            Circuit board
            Wire, solder, etc.
            Control knob

HALL EFFECT SIGNAL/CURRENT TRACING

Linear Hall effect devices are sometimes used in test equipment that measures the current flow in printed circuit tracks without making any direct connection to the tracks. Instead, the Hall effect sensor is used to detect the strength of the magnetic field around the track. The copper tracks themselves are, of course, non-magnetic, and the magnetic field is generated by the current flowing through the track. The larger the current flow, the stronger the magnetic field.

The metered version of the Hall effect compass would seem to be a good basis for a current tracker, since it can detect very weak magnetic fields. In practice it seems to be something less than impressive when used in this way. One problem is that the unit responds to the earth's magnetic field, and that this tends to confuse results. Is a deflection of the meter due to a current passing through the track under test, or the earth's magnetic field? There is no easy way of shielding the sensor from the earth's magnetic field, but keeping it in a horizontal position means that the direction of the field is such that it does not have any significant effect on the sensor.

The main problem is a lack of sensitivity. With a few hundred milliamps passing through a track an increased reading is obtained on one side of the track, and a reduced reading is obtained on the other. With currents of a few milliamps any variations in the readings are so small as to be imperceptible. This type of Hall effect sensor does not seem to be well suited to current tracking applications, but if you have made up the metered version of the Hall effect compass it is interesting to give it a try.

The upper limit of the UGN3505U's frequency response is 23kHz, which makes it suitable for audio signal tracing. Again, the idea is to use the sensor to pick up the magnetic field around the p.c.b. tracks, enabling signals to be traced without making any direct connection to the circuit under test. In theory at any rate, this is easier than d.c. current measurement, because an a.c. coupled amplifier can be used. This makes it possible to use high levels of gain without any d.c. drift problems. The earth's magnetic field is a constant field, and it does not present a major problem with a device that is designed to detect rapidly varying fields.

Figure 7 shows the circuit diagram for the experimental Hall effect signal tracer. The output from the sensor (IC1) is coupled to a common emitter amplifier based on TR1. Due to the local negative feedback provided by R3 this stage exhibits a relatively low voltage gain of about 10 times (20dB). C3 couples the output from TR1 to a second common emitter amplifier which is based on TR2. This does not have an emitter resistor, and it therefore exhibits a high level of voltage gain of around 200 times or more (46dB or more). The output of IC1 is direct coupled to earphone socket JK1, and only a crystal earphone should be plugged into this socket. Trying to use other types of earphone or headphones will not damage the unit, but will almost certainly fail to give significant volume levels. The current consumption of the circuit is about 9 milliamps or so.

The signal tracer works rather better than the d.c. compass circuit used as a d.c. current tracker. However, it is still something less than impressive. The audio noise level from the senor is not particularly low, and when amplified by 60dB or more it produces quite a high "hiss" level from the earphone. Using C4 to apply some high frequency roll-off to the second amplifier stage helps to reduce the noise level slightly, but obviously results in some loss of treble on the output signal. In the present application this loss of high frequency response is probably not of any major importance.

This unit is capable of detecting extremely weak varying magnetic fields. A strong signal, such as that at the output of even a small power amplifier (driving a load) is easily detected. The field generated by an a.c. signal of a few milliamps

16

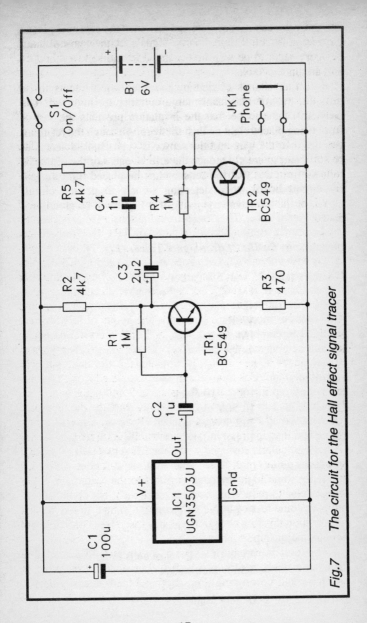

Fig.7   The circuit for the Hall effect signal tracer

17

peak-to-peak can also be detected provided the sensor is placed close against the circuit board. Signals in the sub-milliamp category seem to be well below the unit's noise level though, and are undetectable.

Detecting signals carried by insulated wires seems to be difficult, even if reasonably large currents are involved. The problem seems to be that the insulation prevents the sensor from being placed right against the wire. Although the resultant gap between the wire and the sensor is very small, it seems to be sufficient to greatly reduce the effectiveness of the sensor. It follows from this that the sensor must be placed right against the circuit board when detecting signals in printed circuit tracks, or the effective sensitivity of the unit will be greatly reduced.

Components for Hall Effect Signal Tracer (Fig. 7)

Resistors (all 0.25 watt 5% carbon film)
R1	1M
R2	4k7
R3	470R
R4	1M
R5	4k7

Capacitors
C1	100µ 10V elect
C2	1µ 50V elect
C3	2µ2 50V elect
C4	1n polyester

Semiconductors
IC1	UGN3503U
TR1	BC549
TR2	BC549

Miscellaneous
B1	6 volt (4 × HP7 size cells in holder)
JK1	3.5mm jack socket
S1	SPST min toggle
	Battery connector

Crystal earphone
Case
Circuit board
Wire, solder, etc.

HALL EFFECT AUDIO ISOLATOR

It is sometimes necessary to couple an audio signal from one device to another without having any direct electrical connection between the two units. In days gone by this was mainly done when an item of equipment that had a "live" chassis needed to be connected to a hi-fi amplifier or other unit that had an earthed chassis. These days most television sets, etc., have audio output sockets that make add-on isolators unnecessary, but isolators are still used for other reasons. Probably their main use is where both audio and digital circuits are involved. A direct connection from one unit to another can sometimes result in digital noise finding its way into the audio signal path. An isolated audio coupling helps to avoid stray coupling of digital noise into the audio signal.

Isolated audio couplings can also help to eliminate problems with earth and "hum" loops. Quite high voltages can be developed between the earth connections of two pieces of equipment that have double-insulated mains power supply units and non-earthed chassis. This can result in damage to one or other of the units if they are directly interconnected. An audio isolator can provide a safe coupling between two units of this type as it will withstand the voltage difference, letting both pieces of equipment function normally.

The most simple form of isolator is an audio transformer. However, this method can provide rather mediocre results unless the transformer is a high quality (and expensive) type. Using a transformer is not a very practical proposition any more, as components having suitable characteristics no longer seem to be available. The usual choice these days is a circuit based on an opto-isolator. The problem with this method is that opto-isolators suffer from severe non-linearity. An opto-isolator can only be used to couple a good quality audio signal if some form of encoding/decoding is used. This normally means either

19

a frequency modulation (f.m.) system, or some form of pulse width modulation (p.w.m.) type. In either case the signal passing through the opto-isolator is a digital type, and the linearity through the device is of no significance. The linearity of the system is largely governed by the quality of the encoding and decoding processes. Good results can be obtained, but f.m. and p.w.m. systems require a high quality opto-isolator plus a lot of circuitry.

A linear Hall effect device offers an interesting alternative. In theory it is quite straightforward to feed the audio signal into an inductor, and use a linear Hall effect device to pick up the varying magnetic field. The linearity of the UGN3503U Hall effect sensor is quite good, which makes it possible to obtain good results without resorting to any form of modulation and demodulation. In practice it seems to be possible to obtain reasonable results using quite simple circuits.

The Circuits

Figure 8 shows the circuit diagram for the input section of the Hall effect audio isolator. This is basically just a small audio power amplifier based on an LM386N integrated circuit. Assuming that the circuit will be fed with a fairly high level signal (about 1 volt r.m.s.), the full 20dB voltage gain of IC1 is not required. Therefore, R1 and R2 are used to provide a certain amount of attenuation to prevent IC1 from being driven into clipping. With some signal sources it might be necessary to increase the value of R1 in order to prevent IC1 from being overloaded. C3 and R3 aid good stability, and C2 is a decoupling capacitor for the preamplifier section of IC1.

The output of the amplifier is coupled to the inductor (L1) via d.c. blocking capacitor C5 and current limiting resistor R4. This method is not very efficient, and most of the output power is wasted in R4. It would be more efficient to use a lower power amplifier and a step-down transformer to provide L1 with the low drive voltage/high drive current that it requires. The obvious problem with this method is that it would require a non-standard transformer that could easily compromise results. This method of driving the inductor is inefficient, but it is simple and gives good results. The current consumption of the circuit is only about 4 milliamps under quiescent conditions, but can

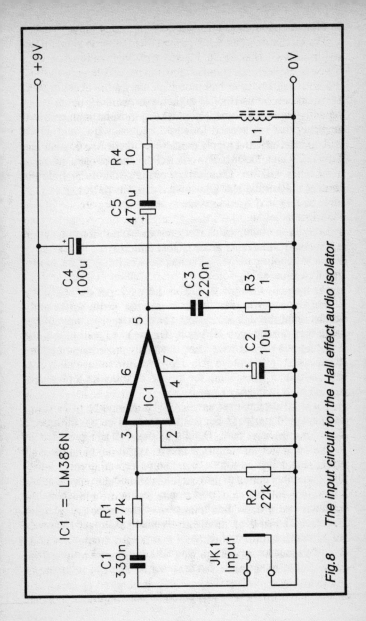

Fig.8   The input circuit for the Hall effect audio isolator

be more than ten times this figure with a strong input signal.

The circuit diagram for the output section of the Hall effect audio isolator appears in Figure 9. This just consists of a UGN3503U Hall effect device feeding into a low gain (6dB or so) inverting amplifier based on IC3. Only a low level of voltage gain can be used since higher gain would give an unacceptably high noise level. Note that IC3 must be an operational amplifier that is intended for audio frequency use, and which will operate well at a supply potential of about 5 to 6 volts. The TLO71CP and TLO81CP work well in this circuit, but most other types will not. The current consumption of the circuit is about 9 to 10 milliamps. Of course, the input and output circuits must be powered from separate supplies if they are to provide electrical isolation.

In order to obtain satisfactory results from this equipment it is necessary to have an inductor that will provide a reasonably efficient coupling to the Hall effect device. In my initial experiments I tried an air-cored coil having about 100 turns of 28 s.w.g. enamelled copper wire. This did work, but the efficiency of the coupling was insufficient to provide anything like unity voltage gain through the system. Next I tried 100 turns of the same wire wound on a 4BA bolt. This worked well in that the coupling was very efficient, and it actually provided something in excess of unity voltage gain. However, the audio quality was less good than when using the air-cored coil, with a relatively limited high frequency response.

The third attempt used another 100 turn winding of 28 s.w.g. enamelled copper wire, but this time wound on a 6 millimetre diameter dust iron core. Details of this coil are provided in Figure 10, which also shows the correct positioning for the Hall effect sensor. It is advisable to use some general purpose adhesive over the winding to prevent it from tending to spring apart. I tried two other sizes of dust iron core, and results seemed to be much the same, so the choice of core size would not seem to be critical. I also tried various ready-made axial lead inductors (r.f. chokes), but most of these gave very little coupling regardless of the sensor's position. One 330µH r.f. choke did actually give quite good results, but the other dozen or so components tried gave unusable results.

Results using the dust iron cored inductors were quite good,

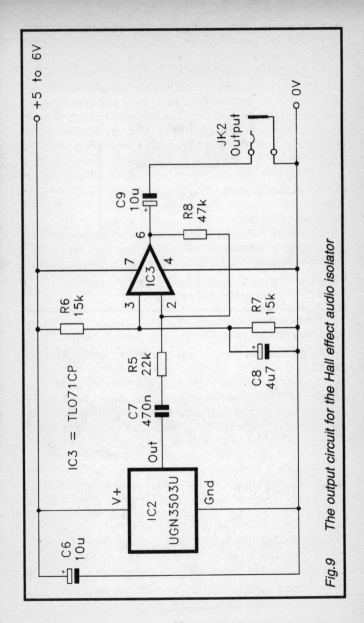

Fig.9   The output circuit for the Hall effect audio isolator

23

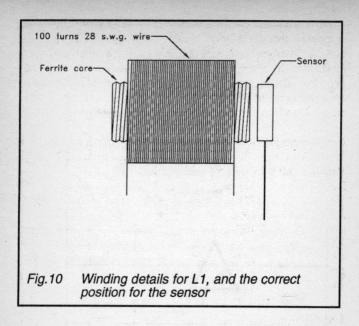

*Fig.10   Winding details for L1, and the correct
position for the sensor*

despite the fact that cores of this type are not intended for audio frequency use. It was quite easy to obtain a sufficiently good coupling to provide more than unity voltage gain through the system. The frequency response was rather flatter than I expected, and held up well at the high end of the audio range. An interesting property of this method of coupling is that it provides no low frequency roll-off, and gives what is actually a form of d.c. coupling. Of course, this is not true of the system as a whole due to the use of coupling capacitors in both the input and output circuits. These provide the usual roll-off in the infra-audio range. It would presumably be quite easy to produce a d.c. coupled version of the system, but I have not tried this.

I did not make any distortion measurements on the system, but the subjective audio quality is quite good, and it is certainly adequate in this respect unless true hi-fi quality is needed. This method certainly seems to offer an interesting and fully viable alternative to the use of an opto-isolator.

Note that if this circuit is used to provide an audio output on equipment that has a "live" chassis, or in any similar application that involves the blocking of high voltages, it should only be installed by someone who has the necessary experience and expertise. The mains supply can be lethal, and only those who are suitably qualified should deal with the mains supply or any other high voltage sources.

Components for Hall Effect Audio Isolator (Figs 8 and 9)

Resistors (all 0.25 watt 5% carbon film)
R1	47k
R2	22k
R3	1R
R4	10R
R5	22k
R6	15k
R7	15k
R8	47k

Capacitors
C1	330n polyester
C2	10μ 25V elect
C3	220n polyester
C4	100μ 10V elect
C5	470μ 10V elect
C6	10μ 25V elect
C7	470n polyester
C8	4μ7 50V elect
C9	10μ 25V elect

Semiconductors
IC1	LM386N
IC2	UGN3503U
IC3	TLO71CP or TLO81CP (see text)

Miscellaneous
JK1	3.5mm jack socket
JK2	3.5mm jack socket
L1	See text

Circuit boards
8 pin DIL IC holder (2 off)
Wire, solder, etc.

HALL EFFECT CURRENT MONITORING

As pointed out in the previous section of this book, an inductor plus a Hall effect sensor provides an isolated link that is capable of operating with direct currents. This property is sometimes exploited to permit currents to be measured without having any direct connection between the main circuit and the current meter circuit. I found that it was quite easy to measure currents in this way using the circuit of Figure 11.

This is really just a slightly modified version of the Hall effect compass that was described previously. The closed loop voltage gain of the amplifier is 40dB (100 times). This is about the maximum voltage gain that should be used, and if possible the value of R4 should be reduced in order to give a lower closed loop gain. This will give better stability with lower drift. VR3 enables the unit to be calibrated, but the sensitivity of the unit is also dependent on the inductor used in the current path, and the distance between the inductor and the Hall effect sensor. Some experimentation is therefore needed in order to get things just right. I would only recommend the use of a "proper" moving coil panel meter in this application. Many "tuning" meters do not have particularly helpful scales when absolute measurement is required, and their linearity is often very poor as well.

The best type of inductor for this application is a slotted ferrite toroid (i.e. a ring of ferrite with a small gap in the ring). The Hall effect sensor fits into the slot in the ferrite ring. Unfortunately, I can find no source for slotted ferrite toroids. Full ferrite toroids are readily available, but cutting a slot into one of these seems to be problematic. Ferrite is an extremely hard and brittle material. Trying to cut through it with a hacksaw usually results in either the hacksaw blade rapidly becoming blunt, or the ferrite ring simply breaking in two.

I therefore tried a few experiments with inductors of the type used with the Hall effect audio isolator project. Even an inductor as basic as 100 turns of wire on a 4BA bolt worked

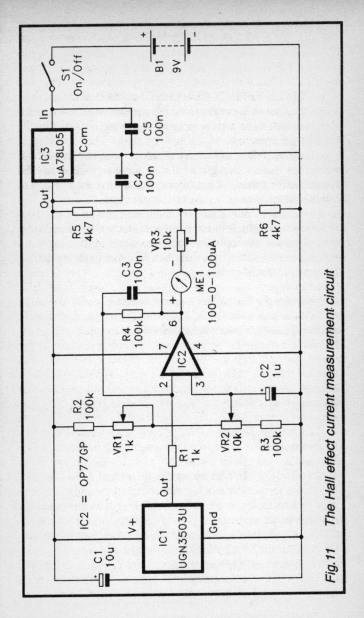

Fig.11   The Hall effect current measurement circuit

27

reasonably well in this application. The frequency response of the system is obviously of no consequence in this case, but linearity is. Bear in mind that most core materials begin to saturate at high currents and they then become relatively inefficient. This would obviously give poor linearity. If the unit is used to monitor high currents the wire used in the inductor must be of suitable thickness for the currents involved, and the core material must also be appropriate to the current flowing through the inductor.

Obtaining full scale values of about plus and minus 100 milliamps is easy enough. Full scale values of one-tenth this figure can be achieved, but higher sensitivities are difficult or impossible to achieve. Linearity is quite good at currents of up to a few tens of milliamps, but at higher currents there was a tendency for readings to fall somewhat short of the true current flow. This was probably due to inadequacies in the core materials I was using rather than any lack of linearity in the Hall effect sensor, amplifier, or meter.

Components for Hall Effect Current Meter (Fig. 11)

Resistors (all 0.25 watt 5% carbon film)

R1	1k
R2	100k
R3	100k
R4	100k
R5	4k7
R6	4k7

Potentiometers

VR1	1k lin carbon
VR2	10k lin carbon
VR3	10k min hor preset

Capacitors

C1	10µ 25V elect
C2	1µ 50V elect
C3	100n polyester
C4	100n ceramic
C5	100n ceramic

Semiconductors

IC1	UGN3503U
IC2	OP77GP or OPA177GP
IC3	μA78L05 5V 100mA pos reg

Miscellaneous

ME1	100-0-100μA moving coil panel meter
B1	9 volt (6 × HP7 size cells in holder)
S1	SPST min toggle
	8 pin DIL IC holder
	Battery connector
	Case
	Materials for inductor (see text)
	Control knob (2 off)
	Circuit board
	Wire, solder, etc.

VOICE SCRAMBLER

No self respecting spy film of the 1960s could have the agents talking to one another over the telephone unless they first pressed the "scramble" button. To anyone listening in on the conversation it was possible to hear nothing more than garbled speech that was totally incomprehensible. The two agents could understand each other without difficulty as they were hearing a descrambled version of the signal.

More recently there has been a lot of interest in this type of thing due to the increased use of mobile telephones. Apparently some telephones use digital technology that prevents anyone listening in using a scanning receiver. Other systems are based on conventional linear techniques, and can be received properly using readily available scanners. There are actually a number of scrambler and descrambler integrated circuits produced, but these are normally not available to amateur users. However, it is possible to produce a reasonably simple scrambler/descrambler using readily available components.

Frequency Inversion

There are several tried and tested methods of scrambling a voice signal, but most of them are too complex to be practical propositions for the home constructor unless the chip sets can be obtained. Fortunately, there is one method which is reasonably simple and effective, and this is the speech inversion method. The basic idea is to process the input signal so that high frequencies are converted to low frequencies, and vice versa. Middle frequencies remain relatively unchanged, although all input frequencies are subjected to some degree of frequency shift.

Although this method is basically quite simple, it is surprisingly effective. No doubt many readers will have used a short wave receiver on the short wave amateur bands. If an upper sideband signal is received as a lower sideband type (or vice versa), the result is something that is clearly recognisable as a human voice. The voice is completely unintelligible though, and in most cases it is not even possible to understand the occasional word here and there. The incorrectly received sideband signal is producing a frequency inverted audio output signal, and is effectively scrambled in '60s spy film fashion.

One way of frequency inverting an audio signal is to convert it into a single sideband signal and then demodulate it as the wrong type of sideband signal. Descrambling the signal is achieved by the same method, so that it is reinverted to restore the original frequencies. I have successfully used this method in the past ("Experimental Electronics", *Practical Electronics*, January 1987), but it has the disadvantage of being relatively expensive. In order to obtain good results it is necessary to use fairly high quality crystal or mechanical filters. These substantially increase the cost of the unit.

There is an alternative method of obtaining a frequency inversion, and this method is relatively inexpensive as it operates entirely at audio frequencies. It requires some reasonably sharp filtering, but the filters are relatively cheap as they are based on resistors, capacitors, and operational amplifiers. Figure 12 shows the block diagram for a scrambler based on this technique.

A buffer amplifier at the input ensures that the following stage is fed from a suitably low source impedance. This following stage is a lowpass filter. The system could be made to operate over the full audio range, but communications systems are usually limited to a bandwidth of about 3.5kHz.

Higher frequencies are not important to the intelligibility of speech. The lowpass filter severely attenuates signals above 3.5kHz, and in this application it is important that these out-of-band signals are severely curtailed as they will otherwise generate distortion products at the output.

The frequency inversion is provided by the next two stages, which are a balanced modulator and a sinewave modulation oscillator which operates at about 4kHz. The modulator is actually a double-balanced type. It combines the input signal with the sinewave signal to produce sum and difference frequencies. The main input and sinewave signals are both balanced out so that they do not appear at the output. The sum signal is the same as the main input signal, but with all the frequencies raised by 4kHz. This signal is not required here, and it is attenuated by the two stage lowpass filter at the output of the unit.

It is the difference signal that provides the frequency inverted signal. Figure 13 helps to explain the way in which this inversion process operates. The diagram at the top shows the input frequencies to the balanced modulator. These are the 4kHz sinewave modulation signal and voice signals at frequencies of 750Hz, 1.5kHz, 2.25kHz, and 3kHz. The four input signals at the audio input are boosted by 4kHz to produce sum frequencies of 4.75kHz, 5.5kHz, 6.25kHz, and 7kHz. The difference frequencies are 3.25kHz, 2.5kHz, 1.75kHz, and 1kHz. These frequency components are shown in the middle diagram. The sum frequencies are removed by the lowpass filtering to leave the difference frequencies (the bottom diagram). As can be seen by comparing the top and bottom diagrams, the difference frequencies provide the frequency inverted and scrambled output signal.

Feeding the scrambled signal through another frequency inverter descrambles the signal, as shown in Figure 14. This time the input frequencies are 3.25kHz, 2.5kHz, 1.75kHz, and 1kHz, giving difference frequencies of 750Hz, 1.5kHz, 2.25kHz, and 3kHz. These are, of course, the original input frequencies.

It is important that the sinewave oscillators in the scrambler and descrambler circuits operate at the same frequencies, or very nearly so. Any difference between their operating frequencies will result in the descrambled audio output signal

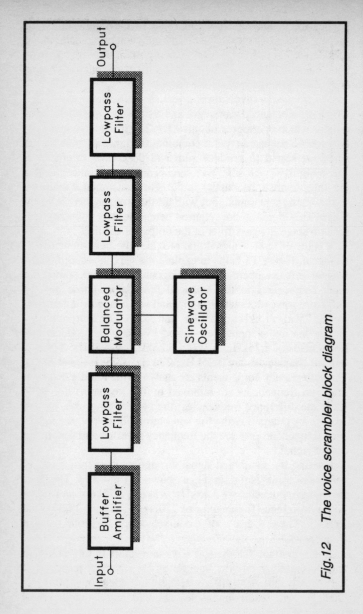

Fig.12   The voice scrambler block diagram

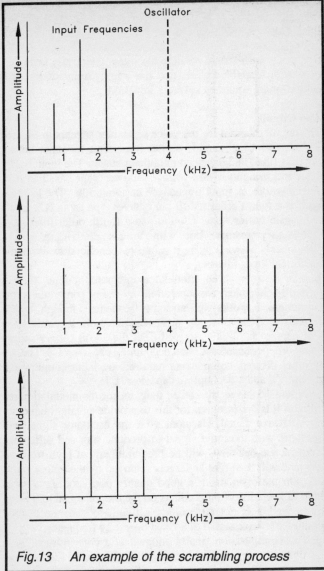

Fig.13   An example of the scrambling process

33

being shifted up or down by an amount that is equal to the frequency difference. Errors of up to about 30Hz or so are not likely to produce any problems, but frequency shifts of about 50Hz or more can produce some odd sounding results. Larger frequency shifts would result in the signal effectively being left in a semi-scrambled state, and the intelligibility of the processed signal would be severely impaired.

The Circuit

The circuit diagram for the voice scrambler appears in Figures 15, 16, and 17. Figure 15 shows the circuit for input buffer, lowpass filter, and balanced modulator stages. The input buffer stage is a straightforward voltage follower stage based on IC1. This provides an input impedance of about 50k. The lowpass filter is a fourth order (24dB per octave) type using IC2 as the unity gain buffer stage. I found that a fourth order filter gave satisfactory results, but with voices containing strong components above 3.5kHz it might be beneficial to use some additional input filtering.

IC3 is a balanced modulator integrated circuit that is primarily intended for operation in radio communications equipment. It works well at audio frequencies though, and is actually well suited to the present application. It requires a 6 volt supply, and this is derived from the 9 volt battery supply using dropper resistor R7 and decoupling capacitor C8. The only other discrete components required are input coupling capacitor C6 and a decoupling capacitor (C7).

Figure 16 shows the circuit diagram for the modulation oscillator. It is not essential for this to provide a really high quality sinewave signal. Harmonics on the oscillator signal will combine with the input signal to produce sum and difference frequencies, but these will be predominantly at high frequencies and will therefore be largely removed by the output filtering. On the other hand, a good quality oscillator signal does help to keep distortion products on the output signal to a minimum, and it is not particularly difficult to generate a good quality sinewave signal at a fixed operating frequency.

The configuration finally adopted is a conventional Wien oscillator having adjustable negative feedback. VR1 is the feedback control, and it is adjusted for sufficient gain to just

34

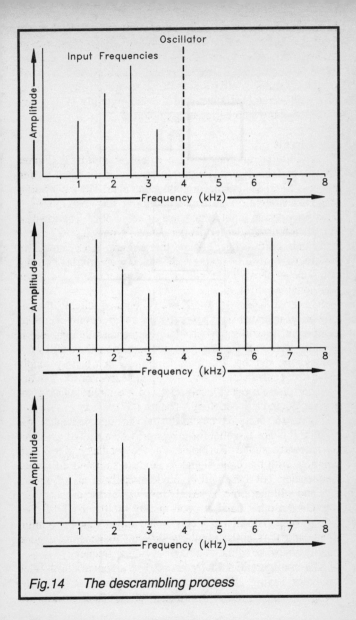

Fig.14   The descrambling process

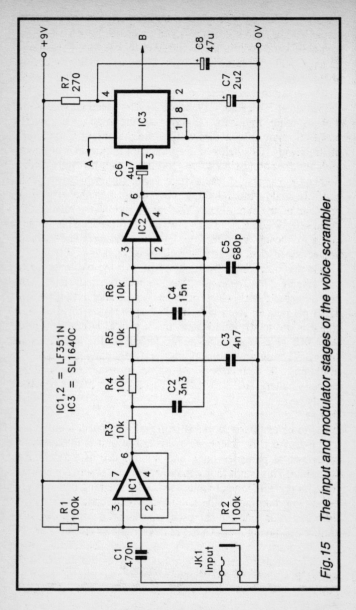

Fig.15   The input and modulator stages of the voice scrambler

36

sustain oscillation. This gives a highly pure sinewave output signal having an amplitude of about 4 volts peak-to-peak. This is slightly excessive for the balanced modulator, so R21 is used in series with the output of IC6 to provide a small amount of attenuation.

The operating frequency of the oscillator is determined by the values of R17, R20, C19, and C20. The specified values set the operating frequency slightly on the high side, which pushes the sum frequencies well above the output filter's cut-off frequency. This helps to keep the sum frequencies at a low level on the output signal. On the other hand, it results in the frequency response of the system being somewhat restricted, and this could impair intelligibility more than the distortion products of the sum signal. You might like to try raising the value of R17 and R20 to 39k or even 47k to reduce the modulation frequency. It is a matter of using the frequency which you consider gives the best overall speech quality.

IC4 and IC5 are the buffer amplifiers in the two output filters (Figure 17). These are conventional four pole and three pole lowpass filters which give an overall attenuation rate of 42dB per octave. Even with filtering as sharp as this the sum signal is not totally eliminated, but it should be reduced to a level that gives acceptable audio quality on the descrambled signal. The current consumption of the unit is about 12 milliamps. It is therefore advisable to use a fairly high capacity battery, such as six HP7 size cells in a plastic holder.

In Use

It has to be emphasised that it is illegal to connect a unit such as this to the U.K. telephone system. The unit is intended for experimental purposes only, and not for use as a telephone scrambler. This is not to say that there are no practical applications for the unit. One obvious use is when making tape recorded notes. Recording via the scrambler would render the tapes of little use to anyone but the user, who could descramble them simply by playing them back via the scrambler circuit.

VR1 must be given the lowest resistance setting that provides reliable operation. The best way of finding the right setting is to use an oscilloscope to monitor the output signal at pin 6 of IC6. Then simply adjust VR1 for a good quality

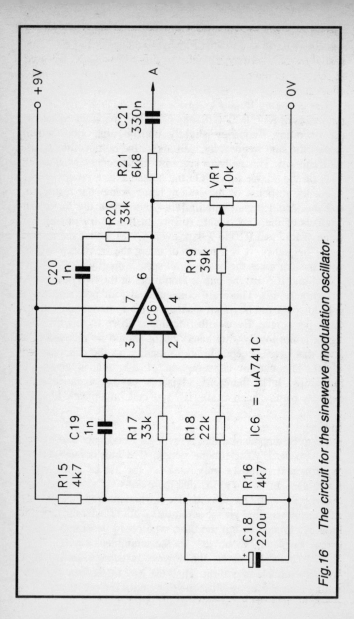

Fig.16 The circuit for the sinewave modulation oscillator

38

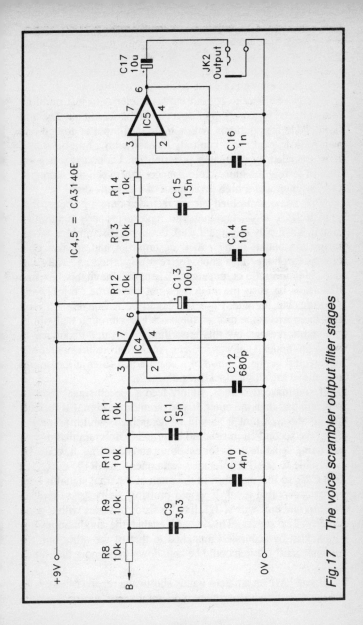

Fig.17 The voice scrambler output filter stages

39

sinewave having an amplitude of about 4 volts peak-to-peak. If you do not have access to an oscilloscope, monitor the output of IC6 using a crystal earphone. Then adjust VR1 for a pure sounding and stable output signal, which will occur with VR1 set just high enough in value to produce oscillation.

The easiest way to try out the scrambler is to just build up one unit, and to record some speech via the scrambler. The unit is intended for operation with a high level input at around one volt peak-to-peak, so it can only be used with a microphone if it is preceded by a suitable preamplifier. I found that a good way of testing the unit was to connect it between the output of a radio tuner and a high level input of a cassette deck.

With some scrambled speech recorded onto a cassette, first play it back to ensure that you have a properly scrambled signal. Then play the signal back through the scrambler, monitoring the output using either an amplifier and speaker or a crystal earphone. This should give a reinverted and fully understandable audio output signal. There will inevitably be some distortion because the unit does not have true "brick-wall" filtering, but the audio quality should be reasonable. I found that there was some discernible clock breakthrough with no input signal present, but this breakthrough became unnoticeable when an input signal was present. An obvious refinement to the unit would be the addition of a sharp notch filter at the output to remove the slight clock breakthrough.

If you make two units, simply feed a speech signal through one unit and then the other. If you monitor the signal at the output of the first unit it should be scrambled, while the output from the second circuit should be properly descrambled. If you are using separate units for encoding and decoding, it would be advisable to use 1% tolerance components for R17, R20, C19 and C20, so that any shift in the pitch of the final signal is kept to an acceptable level. It would probably be better to replace R20 in one unit with a 22k fixed resistor in series with a good quality 22k preset. This would enable the modulation frequency to be accurately matched to that of the other unit, so that any shift in pitch could be kept down to no more than a few hertz.

If you have an amateur bands shortwave receiver there is an interesting little experiment you might like to try. Use the receiver to pick up a single sideband transmission, but set the receiver to the wrong sideband mode (e.g. tune in a lower sideband transmission on the 80 metre band, but with the receiver set to the upper sideband mode). This will, of course, produce a scrambled audio output signal from the receiver. Couple the audio output from the "Tape" or "Phones" socket of the receiver to the input of the scrambler, and monitor the output of the scrambler using a crystal earphone. You should find that the signal can be copied without difficulty if the tuning control of the receiver is adjusted for an audio output of the correct pitch.

Components for Voice Scrambler (Figs 16, 17, and 18)

Resistors (all 0.25 watt 5% carbon film)

R1	100k
R2	100k
R3	10k
R4	10k
R5	10k
R6	10k
R7	270R
R8	10k
R9	10k
R10	10k
R11	10k
R12	10k
R13	10k
R14	10k
R15	4k7
R16	4k7
R17	33k
R18	22k
R19	39k
R20	33k
R21	6k8

Potentiometer

VR1	10k lin carbon

Capacitors

C1	470n polyester
C2	3n3 polyester
C3	4n7 polyester
C4	15n polyester
C5	680p polystyrene
C6	4µ7 50V elect
C7	2µ2 50V elect
C8	47µ 16V elect
C9	3n3 polyester
C10	4n7 polyester
C11	15n polyester
C12	680p polyester
C13	100µ 10V elect
C14	10n polyester
C15	15n polyester
C16	1n polyester
C17	10µ 25V elect
C18	220µ 10V elect
C19	1n polyester
C20	1n polyester
C21	330n polyester

Semiconductors

IC1	LF351N
IC2	LF351N
IC3	SL1640C
IC4	CA3140E
IC5	CA3140E
IC6	µA741C

Miscellaneous

JK1	3.5mm jack socket
JK2	3.5mm jack socket
	Circuit board
	Case
	8 pin DIL IC holder (6 off)
	Control knob
	Wire, solder, etc.

ULTRASONIC DETECTOR

Although no human can hear sounds at frequencies of more than about 20kHz, there are certainly plenty of sounds around us at frequencies of 20kHz to about 100kHz. It would often be interesting or useful to have a unit that would enable sounds in this range to be heard, after a fashion, by humans. Apparently units of this type are sometimes used in industry, mainly to aid the detection of small gas leaks (which produce sounds that are predominantly in the ultrasonic region).

For amateur users the main application is in the field of nature study. In particular, units of this type can be used to detect the ultrasonic sounds emitted by bats when using their echo location systems. It is also possible to detect other animal sounds, and many insects produce sounds at ultrasonic frequencies. This apparently includes certain moths and a few other insects which have the ability to jam a bat's ultrasonic radar.

An ultrasonic sound detector can also be used for general experimentation purposes. There is a surprisingly large amount of ultrasonic sound in the average environment. In general, large objects such as pieces of furniture do not produce much ultrasonic output, even if moved around in a heavy-handed fashion. On the other hand, small objects often seem to produce more sound at ultrasonic frequencies than at audio frequencies. Dropping a pin onto a hard surface for example, seems to produce an easily detected ultrasonic noise.

There are two possible approaches to bringing ultrasonic frequencies within the audio range. One of these is to use a system of frequency division. Digital frequency division is easy enough, but is less than ideal in the current context. The received signal would have to be clipped and fed to a divider chain. The output from the divider would be a squarewave at (say) one-tenth of the input frequency. I suppose that this method would give reasonable results with simple single tone inputs, but it would not work properly with more complex input signals.

The alternative method, and the one adopted here, is a system which uses a heterodyning technique. Figure 18 shows the block diagram for the ultrasonic detector. The microphone represents a major problem because normal microphones have frequency responses that roll-off fairly rapidly above about 10 to 20 kHz. This renders them of little use in the present application. A few experiments showed that ultrasonic transducers of the type used in remote control units operate reasonably efficiently over most of the 20kHz to 100kHz range, and it is therefore a transducer of this type that is used as the microphone. The frequency response of an ultrasonic transducer is far from flat, and can usually be relied upon to contain numerous peaks and troughs. In practice results seem to be quite reasonable despite the unit's relative "deafness" at certain frequencies. Being realistic about it, there is no alternative unless you can find an ordinary microphone that has a response which extends well above the audio range (which is highly unlikely). Even if you could locate a source for such a component it would probably be prohibitively expensive.

A low noise preamplifier boosts the output signal from the microphone, and then the signal is fed to a highpass filter. The ultrasonic transducer only operates as a very inefficient microphone at audio frequencies, but the highpass filter helps to further reduce the efficiency of the circuit at these lower frequencies, which in turn reduces the risk of audio frequencies breaking through at the output. Next the signal is fed to a lowpass filter. This helps to avoid problems with stray pick up of radio frequency signals.

An amplifier stage boosts the filtered signal to a suitable level to drive the next stage, which is a balanced modulator. Like the balanced modulator in the voice scrambler unit described previously, it heterodynes the input signal with the output of an oscillator to produce sum and difference frequencies. Also like the voice scrambler unit, the sum signal is removed by a lowpass filter at the output as it is only the difference signal that is required.

Suppose that a bat's radar is using a frequency of 50kHz. If the oscillator is tuned to a frequency of 49kHz the difference frequency would be 1kHz, bringing the signal into the middle audio range where it would be clearly audible. Tuning the oscillator to 51kHz would have the same effect, and in practice it does not matter which side of the input frequency the oscillator is tuned. It is simply given any setting that produces an audio output at a middle audio frequency.

A big advantage of the heterodyne method is that it is able to cope with complex input signals. Suppose that the input is a noise signal from about 40kHz to 50kHz. Tuning the oscillator to a frequency of 39kHz would give an audio noise output signal at frequencies from 1kHz to 11kHz. No matter how complex the input signal, this method can always convert it to a comparable audio signal. The only restriction is that the audio range is about 20kHz wide, and the unit can therefore cover no more than a 20kHz wide portion of the ultrasonic range at any one time.

The Circuit
The circuit diagram for the ultrasonic detector appears in Figures 19 to 21. Taking Figure 19 first, the microphone is direct coupled to the input of a high gain common emitter amplifier based on TR1. The output from this stage is coupled to volume control VR1, and then to a third order (18dB per octave) highpass filter which has IC1 as the buffer amplifier. C6 couples the output of IC1 to the second amplifier stage, which is another common emitter type. C7 provides a small amount of lowpass filtering which helps to avoid problems with r.f. breakthrough.

When using the unit you must bear in mind that ultrasonic sounds are highly directional. The microphone must therefore be aimed at the "target" with reasonable accuracy. Sounds beamed in your direction will be much easier to pick up than those aimed away from you. Also bear in mind that the microphone is only designed for use at around 40kHz, and is only guaranteed to operate efficiently close to this frequency. In practice results seem to be reasonable over a much wider frequency range, but the frequency response of the transducer is full of peaks and troughs. Consequently it is very sensitive at some frequencies, but is virtually "deaf" to others.

Components for Ultrasonic Detector (Figs 19, 20 and 21)

Resistors (all 0.25 watt 5% carbon film)
R1   1M2
R2   2k7
R3   3k9

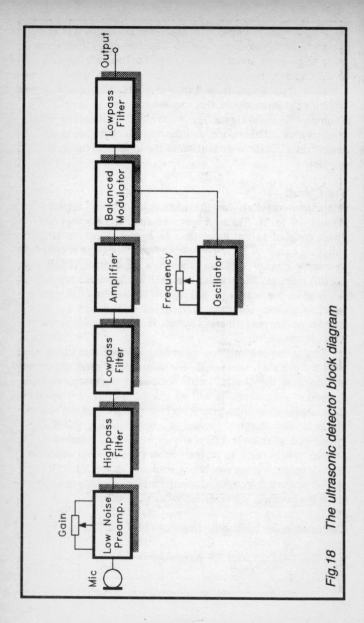

Fig.18   The ultrasonic detector block diagram

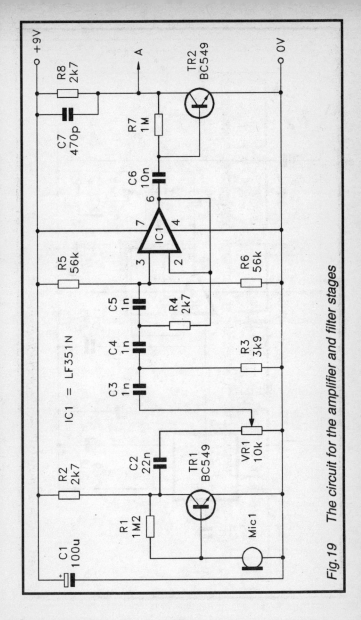

Fig.19 The circuit for the amplifier and filter stages

47

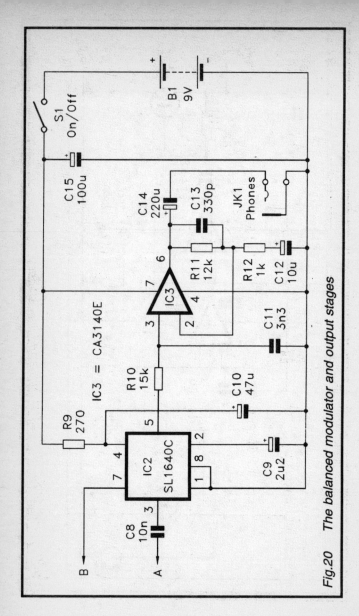

Fig.20 The balanced modulator and output stages

48

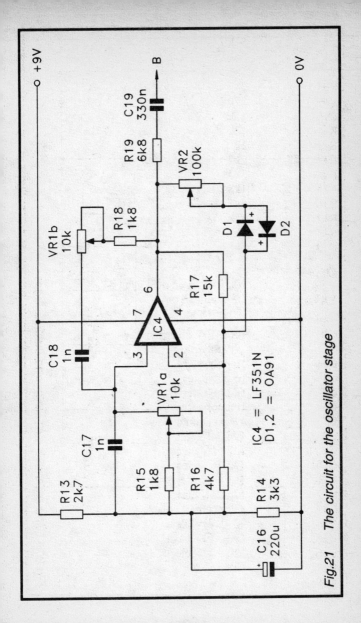

Fig.21   The circuit for the oscillator stage

49

R4	2k7
R5	56k
R6	56k
R7	1M
R8	2k7
R9	270R
R10	15k
R11	12k
R12	1k
R13	2k7
R14	3k3
R15	1k8
R16	4k7
R17	15k
R18	1k8
R19	6k8

Potentiometers

VR1	10k lin carbon dual gang
VR2	100k lin carbon

Capacitors

C1	100µ 10V elect
C2	22n polyester
C3	1n polyester
C4	1n polyester
C5	1n polyester
C6	10n polyester
C7	470p ceramic plate
C8	10n polyester
C9	2µ2 50V elect
C10	47µ 16V elect
C11	3n3 polyester
C12	10µ 25V elect
C13	330p ceramic plate
C14	220µ 10V elect
C15	100µ 10V elect
C16	220µ 10V elect
C17	1n polyester
C18	1n polyester
C19	330n polyester

Semiconductors

IC1	LF351N
IC2	SL1640C
IC3	CA3140E
IC4	LF351N
TR1	BC549
TR2	BC549
D1	OA91
D2	OA91

Miscellaneous

Mic1	40kHz ultrasonic transducer (see text)
JK1	3.5mm jack socket
B1	9 volt ($6 \times$ HP7 size cells in holder)
S1	SPST miniature toggle
	Crystal earphone or medium impedance headphones
	8 pin DIL IC holder (4 off)
	Control knob (2 off)
	Wire, solder, etc.

BREEZE DETECTOR

Probably most readers are familiar with security lights, intruder detectors, etc., which use pyro sensors and special lenses to detect the body heat of anyone within the monitored zone. A practical sensor of this type is actually a little more than just the basic ceramic sensing element, and there are usually one or two ceramic elements plus a source follower buffer stage. Figure 22 shows the internal circuits for single (a) and dual (b) element sensors.

Manufacturers' data sometimes show the ceramic elements of twin element sensors connected in parallel rather than in series, but in either case they are connected in anti-phase so that the signal from the background infra-red is equal but opposite from the two sensors, and is cancelled out. The system is arranged so that anyone entering the protected zone is detected by one element and then the other, giving two "blips" of output signal having opposite polarity. Although load resistor Rb is shown as being an internal part of the sensor, with many practical pyro sensors this is actually an external component.

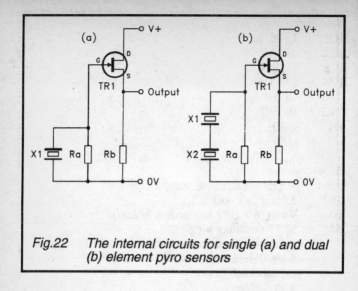

Fig.22   The internal circuits for single (a) and dual
(b) element pyro sensors

Wind of Change

Probably most readers are unaware that a slightly modified version of the pyro sensor can be used to detect small changes in air pressure. The general idea is for sensors of this type to be used in intruder detectors where they detect the change in pressure when someone opens a door to enter. In fact intruder alarms of this type can be very sensitive, enabling them to detect the slight breeze caused by someone passing close to the sensor. Even someone breathing in and out close to the sensor can be enough to trigger the alarm.

The way in which this form of sensor works is something less than obvious, and I have never come across an official explanation from a manufacturer. Indeed, I have never seen any published information on this topic. The sensors themselves seem to differ from standard pyro sensors only in the form of their encapsulations. The two examples I was given to "play" with some years ago have standard TO5 metal type encapsulations, but without the usual "window". One device is of the "large" variety, and it has a relatively large hole in the top where the "window" would normally be found. The actual

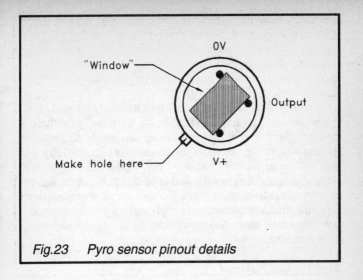

Fig.23   Pyro sensor pinout details

diameter of the hole would seem to be about 3 to 3.5 milli-metres. The other sensor has a small hole of about 0.7 millimetres in diameter in its side, near to the metal tab.

Possibly the change in temperature to activate the sensor is caused by a slight increase or decrease in pressure causing a slight rise or fall in temperature. Alternatively, air turbulence in the room might cause local turbulence around the sensor, re-sulting in new air at a slightly different temperature passing over the sensing element or elements. Either way, sensors of this type do work, and are quite sensitive. The sensor having the larger hole seems to be particularly sensitive, and must be used with far less gain than a conventional pyro sensor.

This is clearly a very interesting type of sensor for the ex-perimenter, but I do not know of a source for this form of py-ro detector. This begs the question "is it possible to convert a conventional pyro sensor to operate as an air pressure change detector?" This is certainly possible, but there is obviously a certain amount of risk involved in tampering with a delicate device such as a pyro sensor. It can be done, but the pyro sensor will be ruined if you are a bit careless or simply get unlucky. I would not recommend buying pyro sensors with a view to converting them into pressure change detectors unless it really is a case of "money is no object". The exception to this would be if you get the opportunity to buy some inexpensive surplus pyro sensors, or some cheap surplus gear that contains them.

If you have some pyro sensors which have been used in experiments and you have no further use for them, then there is clearly little to lose by trying a conversion job. In all probability you will convert them to pressure sensors successfully, and will get some further "mileage" out of them. In any event, neither the publisher nor the author of this publication will accept any responsibility if you try to convert pyro sensors to air pressure change detectors and simply end up with some expensive high-tech junk. Any modifications are made entirely at your own risk.

Modification Methods
The easy part of modifying a pyro sensor for use as a pressure change detector is covering up the "window" so that the device does not generate spurious signals due to changes in the detected infra-red level. In practice this will not always be necessary, as in normal use the sensor may well be within a case that will shield it from any infra-red in the outside world. If not, it is simply a matter of placing a piece of insulation tape, Bostik Blu-Tack, or anything that is opaque to infra-red over the "window". Long wavelength infra-red has the ability to pass through many materials that are opaque to visible light, but anything fairly thick and opaque should effectively shield the sensing element from any ambient infra-red.

The more difficult aspect of conversion is making a hole in the case of the sensor without damaging any of the components within the case. The internal components of a pyro sensor seem to be largely immune to damage by physical shock, but anything penetrating the case and touching any of the components or internal wiring is more or less guaranteed to render the device unusable. The obvious way of tackling the problem is to simply smash the "window", but however carefully I tried to do this, I never succeeded in getting a usable device. There is usually very little clearance between the "window" and the internal components of the pyro sensor, which makes it virtually impossible to penetrate the "window" without also damaging the interior of the sensor.

Much better results were obtained by drilling a small hole of about one millimetre in diameter in the side of the case. It is virtually impossible to drill a hole in the curved metal surface of the case, so a small area of casing must be flattened first, or be punched with a small indentation. I found that the easiest way of doing this was to grip the sensor in the grooved jaws of a "Workmate", and then use a small hammer plus a nail about 50 millimetres long to punch a small indentation in the side of the case near to the tab. Figure 23 shows the pinout arrangement for a pyro sensor having a TO5 style case, and it also shows the position for the hole.

Once the indentation has been made, the hole is easily made using a small hand or power drill fitted with a bit of about one millimetre in diameter. Whichever type of drill you use, it is essential to proceed very carefully so that the drill bit is not allowed to penetrate the sensor's case by more than a millimetre or two. Make frequent checks on the progress of the drilling, and proceed very slowly and carefully once it is apparent that the drill bit is starting to penetrate the case. I found that this method gave a 100% success rate provided I used due care and attention. The success rate was 0% if I took a more "bull in a china shop" approach.

I found a less neat but equally effective method was to simply grip the sensor in the "Workmate", and then use a hacksaw to cut into the edge of the case above the tab. This does not produce particularly neat results, but it is relatively easy to ensure that no damage occurs to the interior of the sensor. Obviously you should cut no deeper than is necessary in order to produce a small hole through the case.

With either method there is a potential flaw in that bits of swarf can easily fall inside the case. The bits of swarf are conductive, and could obviously produce problems. There is not really much that can be done to guard against this, but in practice it does not seem to be a major problem. I successfully completed a number of conversions without any apparent problems due to internal short circuits, etc., caused by particles of casing.

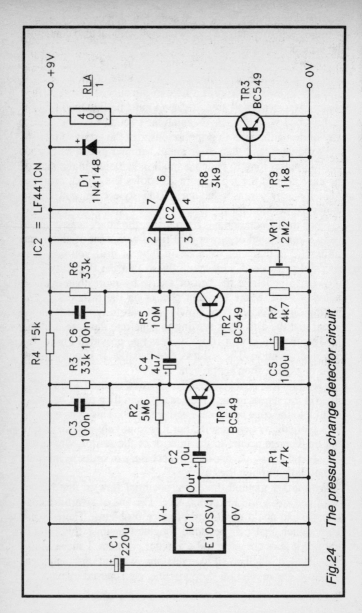

Fig.24   The pressure change detector circuit

56

There is another potential problem in that the open nature of a modified sensor could reduce the life expectancy of the sensor. The devices I modified a few years ago are still working, although one or two seem to be relatively insensitive. Again, there is not really a great deal that can be done to combat this problem, and it simply has to be accepted that a modified senor is likely to have inferior long term reliability when compared to an unmodified component.

Detector Circuit

The modified pyro sensor is used in circuits of the same basic type that are used for non-modified devices. The two circuits featured here are largely "borrowed" from conventional pyro detector circuits in the book "Practical Opto-Electronic Projects" (BP349) which is from the same publisher and author as this publication.

The circuit of Figure 24 is for a basic detector that activates a relay when a change in pressure is detected. IC1 is the modified pyro sensor, and although it is specified as being a E100SV1, any pyro sensor that has been modified correctly should work properly in this circuit. R1 is the discrete load resistor for the built-in source follower stage of IC1. This might not be needed with some other types of pyro sensor, but having both internal and discrete load resistors should not have a substantial effect on performance.

TR1 and TR2 are used in a two stage common emitter amplifier which substantially boosts the output signal from the sensor. This amplifier is capable of providing a total voltage gain of around 80dB, but with many sensors this will result in excessive sensitivity. Some local negative feedback has therefore been introduced to TR2 by the addition of emitter resistor R7. This reduces the voltage gain of TR2 to something under 20dB (10 times).

With some sensors this will give rather low sensitivity, and the value of R7 must then be reduced in order to boost the sensitivity to an acceptable level. You may prefer to use a 4k7 preset for R7, so that the gain of the amplifier can be trimmed to the optimum level. Whichever method of gain trimming you adopt, it is better to err on the side of caution and set the gain fractionally lower than the maximum acceptable level. Setting the gain slightly too high will result in frequent spurious triggering, which in most applications will render the unit worse than useless. The amplifier only has to deal with frequencies in the sub-audio range. C3 and C6 are therefore used to roll-off the response of the circuit at higher frequencies, which gives a worthwhile reduction in its output noise level.

IC2 operates as a voltage detector. Its non-inverting input is fed a reference voltage provided by VR1, and its inverting input is fed from the output of TR2. VR1 is set for a wiper voltage that is slightly higher than the quiescent output voltage at TR2's collector. Thus, under standby conditions the output of IC1 is low, TR3 is cut off, and the relay is not activated. When the unit is activated the voltage at TR2's collector will vary either side of its quiescent level, and on negative excursions it will go below the reference voltage at the non-inverting input of IC2. The output of IC2 then goes high, switching on both TR3 and the relay.

The relay can be any type which has a 6 volt coil with a resistance of about 200R or more, plus suitable contacts for your particular application. This circuit does not provide latching, and the relay contacts will therefore only close momentarily when the unit is activated. In most applications this will not matter, as the unit will be used with additional circuitry that will (where necessary) provide a latching action. For example, the circuit could be used as a sensor for a burglar alarm installation. The main alarm circuit will then provide latching, entry and exit delays, etc. The current consumption of the circuit is well under one milliamp under standby conditions, but it is around 25 to 40 milliamps when the relay is activated.

When using this sensor it is important to realise that it takes several seconds after switch on before the voltages settle down at their normal operating levels, and the units starts to function properly. This abnormally long settling time is due to the relatively large coupling capacitors that must be used in order to give the circuit a frequency response that extends well into the sub audio range.

The relay should switch on if VR1 is initially set for almost maximum wiper voltage. If VR1 is slowly adjusted to give a decreasing wiper voltage, at some point the relay should switch off. VR1 should be backed off a little further from this point, and the unit should then function reliably. As an initial test, try blowing on the sensor. This should produce a large voltage swing at TR2's collector, causing the relay to switch on again for a short while. I found that the prototype sensor was very sensitive, and it easily detected doors being opened or someone passing close to the sensor.

Components for Air Pressure Change Detector (Fig. 24)

Resistors (all 0.25 watt 5% carbon film)

R1	47k
R2	5M6
R3	33k
R4	15k
R5	10M
R6	33k
R7	4k7
R8	3k9
R9	1k8

Potentiometer

VR1	2M2 min hor preset

Capacitors

C1	220µ 16V elect
C2	10µ 25V elect
C3	100n polyester
C4	4µ7 50V elect
C5	100µ 16V elect
C6	100n polyester

Semiconductors

IC1	E100SV1 pyro sensor (or similar)
IC2	LF441CN
TR1	BC549
TR2	BC549
TR3	BC549
D1	1N4148

6 volt coil, 200R or greater coil resistance
(see text)
8 pin DIL IC holder
Circuit board
Wire, solder, etc.

PRESSURE CHANGE ALARM

This circuit is for a self-contained alarm which is based on the pressure change detector circuit described previously. The unit is intended to operate as a burglar deterrent for use where the cost of a comprehensive burglar alarm system is not warranted. As the unit is small and self-contained it is well suited to use in a caravan or boat. It provides a "beep-beep" alarm signal from a Piezo sounder when a change in air pressure is detected.

Figure 25 shows the block diagram for the passive infra-red alarm. The top row of four blocks form the basic pressure change detector, and this part of the unit is essentially the same as the pressure change detector described previously, but with the relay and relay driver omitted. The output of the level detector drives a latch. Even though the output of the level detector will only go high momentarily when the unit is activated, the latch will provide a continuous high output level once "set" by an output pulse from the level detector. The latch activates an LFO (low frequency oscillator), which in turn gates an audio frequency oscillator. Once the unit is activated, the LFO therefore pulses the audio oscillator on and off. This generates a "beep-beep" alarm sound from the loudspeaker (a piezo sounder) driven from the output of the audio oscillator.

There is a problem with this arrangement in that the level detector tends to produce output pulses for a few seconds after switch-on. This occurs while the coupling capacitors in the circuit take up their normal operating charges. This would make the unit trigger almost immediately at switch-on, which would clearly render it completely useless. A hold-off is needed, so that the unit can not trigger for the first few seconds after switch-on. This also gives the user a chance to switch on the unit and get away without activating the alarm. The hold-off is

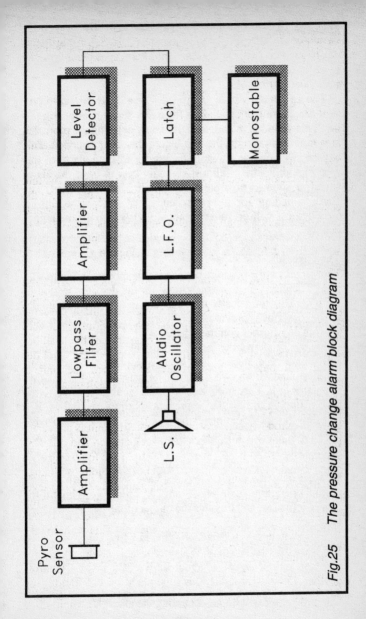

Fig.25   The pressure change alarm block diagram

61

provided by a monostable which automatically triggers at switch-on. It holds the latch in the "reset" state for a little under 10 seconds, which gives the amplifier stages plenty of time to settle down, and the user ample time to switch on and get well clear of the unit.

The unit could also be equipped with a delay circuit to prevent the alarm from sounding for a few seconds after triggering. This would give people legitimately entering the protected area time to switch off the unit before the alarm sounded. This is probably not a worthwhile feature for a small alarm of this type though, and it is almost certainly best to have the alarm sound as soon as possible when an intruder is detected. The alarm sounding for a few seconds just before the unit is switched off will presumably not seriously disturb the neighbours.

The Circuit

The circuit for the pressure change alarm appears in Figures 26 and 27. Figure 26 shows the circuit for the detector section of the unit. This is basically the same as the pressure change detector described previously (Figure 24), and it does not warrant any further comment here.

Figure 27 shows the circuit for the alarm generator, latch, and monostable stages. The latch is a basic SR (set–reset) flip/flop made from two of the NOR gates in IC4. The other two gates in IC4 are not used, but their inputs are wired to the 0 volt supply rail in order to prevent spurious operations. IC3 is a low power 555 timer which is used in the monostable mode. R8 and C7 provide a trigger pulse at switch-on, and IC3's output then goes high for a time determined by R9 and C8 (about 9.5 seconds). This ensures that the latch is in the reset state once the amplifier stages have settled down to their normal operating conditions. Point "A" briefly goes high if the unit is activated, and this sets the output of the latch to the high state.

This switches on IC5, which is the low frequency oscillator. IC5 is used in the standard 555 gated astable mode, and it provides an output signal at about 2.5Hz. IC5 in turn controls another 555 gated astable, this time based on IC6 and having an output frequency of nearly 2kHz. IC6 directly drives a

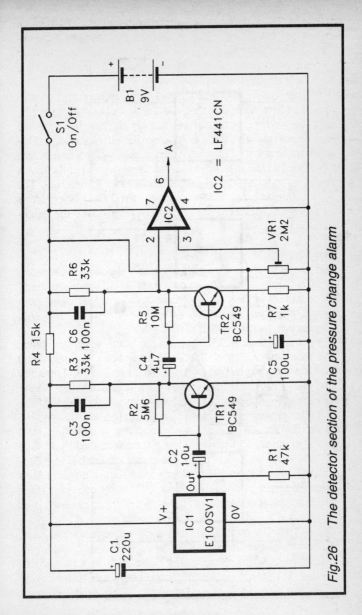

Fig.26   The detector section of the pressure change alarm

63

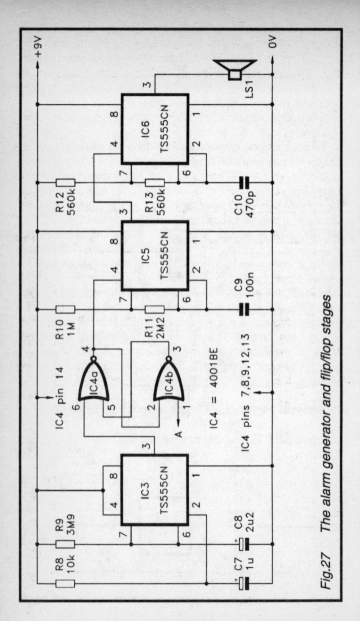

Fig.27   The alarm generator and flip/flop stages

64

ceramic resonator which produces a burst of tone each time IC6 is switched on. Do not use an ordinary moving coil loudspeaker for LS1. The ceramic resonator should provide high efficiency at the relatively high operating frequency of IC6, but if desired the value of C10 can be "tweaked" to give optimum volume. Cased ceramic resonators can provide surprisingly high volume levels when fed with signals at suitable frequencies.

The current consumption of the circuit under standby conditions is only about 500 to 600 microamps. This rises to a few milliamps when the alarm is activated. Although the circuit has a very low standby current consumption, it is still necessary to use a fairly high capacity battery. Bear in mind that in normal use the unit will be left switched on for many hours at a time. Six HP7 (AA) size cells in a plastic holder are probably the best choice. Under standby conditions each set of batteries should provide over two thousand hours of continuous use.

When constructing the unit bear in mind that the 4001BE used for IC4 is a CMOS device, and that it therefore requires the normal anti-static handling precautions. VR1 is given a setting that produces a reference voltage that does not give false alarms from the unit. The positioning of the alarm within the protected room does not seem to be critical. It should readily detect someone opening a door and entering the room wherever it is placed within the room.

Components for Pressure Change Alarm (Figs 26 and 27)

Resistors (all 0.25 watt 5% carbon film)

R1	47k
R2	5M6
R3	33k
R4	15k
R5	10M
R6	33k
R7	1k
R8	10k
R9	3M9
R10	1M
R11	2M2

R12	560k
R13	560k

Potentiometer

VR1	2M2 min hor preset

Capacitors

C1	220µ 16V elect
C2	10µ 25V elect
C3	100n polyester
C4	4µ7 50V elect
C5	100µ 16V elect
C6	100n polyester
C7	1µ 50V elect
C8	2µ2 50V elect
C9	100n polyester
C10	470p ceramic plate

Semiconductors

IC1	E100SV1 pyro sensor (or similar)
IC2	LF441CN
IC3	TS555CN (or similar low power 555)
IC4	4001BE
IC5	TS555CN
IC6	TS555CN
TR1	BC549
TR2	BC549

Miscellaneous

LS1	Cased ceramic resonator
S1	SPST min toggle
B1	9 volt (6 HP7 size cells in holder)
	Battery clip (PP3 type)
	Case
	8 pin DIL IC holder (4 off)
	14 pin DIL IC holder
	Circuit board
	Wire, solder, etc.

INFRA-RED DETECTOR

Although this device was only designed for experimental purposes, units of this type do have practical uses, particularly in the security field. It is designed to detect long wavelength infra-red, and in practical applications this usually means the body heat of a person. The unit is used rather like a torch, and it is scanned slowly from side to side as if you were looking for someone in a torch beam. However, rather than shining a beam of light, the unit "looks" down a narrow corridor, and flashes a LED indicator if someone is detected. The advantage of this system is that you can detect the presence of someone without them knowing that they have been detected. Indeed, they may not even be aware that you are looking for them.

The block diagram of Figure 28 helps to explain the basic way in which the unit functions. The pyro sensor has a fairly wide angle of view, making it unsuitable for use in the present application unless some form of optical system is used to produce a narrower response angle. The most simple way of achieving this is to use a piece of tubing to give the sensor "tunnel vision". This enables the angle of view to be narrowed down to a few degrees if desired, but it gives relatively low sensitivity. Indeed, the range of the unit would probably be no more than two or three metres. Much better results are obtained using a lens.

This produces a major difficulty in that ordinary lenses do not work well at the long infra-red wavelengths involved in this application. In fact most lenses seem to be virtually opaque to long wavelength infra-red, and none that I have tried have focused properly with this type of "light". Fortunately, a special lens is available (the Chartland Electronics CE01), and this provides the unit with a narrow angle of view and excellent sensitivity. In fact it will work at a maximum range of about 20 metres or more. The CE01 has a focal length of approximately 30 millimetres, which means that the pyro sensor must be positioned centrally about 30 millimetres behind the lens (Figure 29). The lens gathers up infra-red energy over a relatively large area and concentrates it onto the pyro sensor. It is the increased "light" gathering power provided by the lens that gives the greatly boosted maximum operating range.

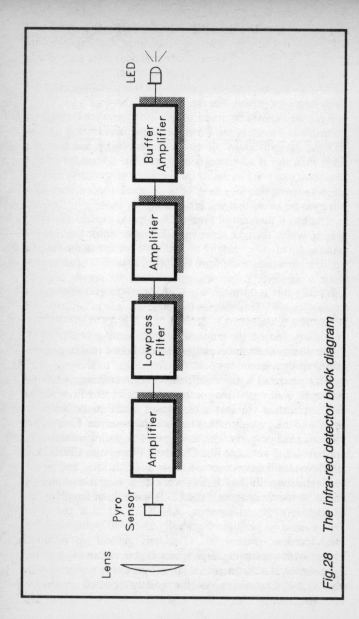

Fig.28   The infra-red detector block diagram

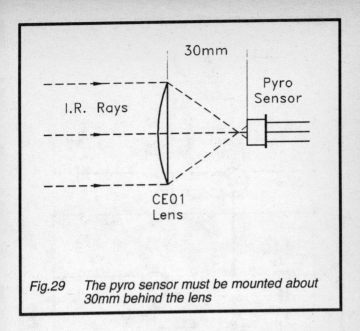

*Fig.29   The pyro sensor must be mounted about
30mm behind the lens*

The electronics consists of little more than a two stage high gain amplifier. Some lowpass filtering helps to minimise the output noise level, and a simple buffer stage enables a LED indicator to be driven from the output of the second amplifier. Under quiescent conditions the output of the amplifier is at about half the supply potential. When someone is detected within the unit's "beam" the output voltage varies between little more than 0 volts and virtually the full supply potential. This causes the LED to flash up and down in brightness. The signal frequencies involved in this application are very low at around 1Hz, and the flashing of the LED is easily perceived by the user.

The Circuit
Figure 30 shows the circuit diagram for the infra-red detector. IC1 is the pyro sensor, and the specified type is a special type which has the two sensing elements in a sort of 69 configuration. The point of this is that the orientation of the sensor is

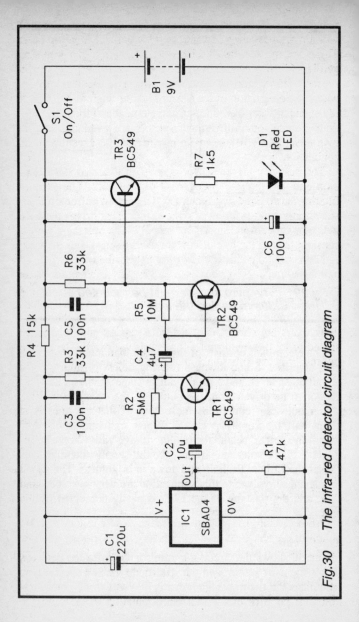

Fig.30   The infra-red detector circuit diagram

70

unimportant. If an infra-red signal is swept across the sensor it will always pass over one sensing element and then the other. Therefore, the sensor will always provide an output signal regardless of the direction in which the signal is swept across the sensor. This is not the case with most two element sensors, where the orientation of the sensor must be such that the infrared signals passes over one sensing element and then the other. Four element omni-directional sensors are available, but the twin element SBA04 seems to provide the best results in this application.

The output from the sensor is coupled to a two stage common emitter amplifier based on TR1 and TR2. The lowpass filtering is provided by C3 and C5. The output buffer amplifier is a simple emitter follower stage (TR3). This drives the LED indicator via current limiting resistor R7. The quiescent current consumption of the circuit is about 3 milliamps, but the average consumption can be somewhat higher than this when the unit is activated. Nevertheless, a PP3 battery is adequate as the power source.

The CE01 lens has a rim which enables it to be glued behind a 30 millimetre diameter hole made in the front of the case. I think that I am correct in stating that this Fresnel lens is designed to be used with the ribbed surface towards the sensor, but results seem to be much the same whichever way round it is fitted. The sensor must be mounted about 30 millimetres behind the lens, and it should be centred as accurately as possible. The unit will still work if the sensor is slightly off-centre, but it will not be "looking" in quite the direction you expect. You may prefer to mount the sensor slightly too far back from the lens. This will give the unit a slightly wider angle of view which will make it a little easier to use. The price that is paid for this is a reduction in the maximum operating range. You might like to experiment a little here to find the best compromise position for the sensor.

When the unit is switched on it takes a few seconds for the coupling capacitors to take up their normal operating charges, and for the unit to function properly. During this "warm up" period there will probably be some random flashing from the LED indicator. Once the unit has settled down it should be easy to detect a helper standing several metres away. The unit is designed for use in darkness, but it will work perfectly well if you test it in daylight. Scan slowly with the unit as the sensor has a very limited upper frequency response (about 3Hz or so). If you scan quickly from side to side the infra-red signals reaching the sensor may be so brief that it fails to respond to them. Bear in mind that the unit does not detect people as such, but detects body heat, or any other sources of heat. It will therefore respond to a radiator, dog, or anything that is warmer than its surroundings.

Components for Infra-Red Detector (Fig. 30)

Resistors (all 0.25 watt 5% carbon film)

R1	47k
R2	5M6
R3	33k
R4	15k
R5	10M
R6	33k
R7	1k5

Capacitors

C1	220µ 10V elect
C2	10µ 25V elect
C3	100n polyester
C4	4µ7 50V elect
C5	100n polyester
C6	100µ 10V elect

Semiconductors

IC1	SBA04 pyro sensor
TR1	BC549
TR2	BC549
TR3	BC549
D1	Red panel LED

Miscellaneous

S1	SPST min toggle
B1	9 volt (PP3 size)
	Lens type CE01

Battery clip
Case
Circuit board
Wire, solder, etc.

The SBA04 pyro sensor and CE01 lens are available from Chartland Electronics Ltd, Chartland House, Old Station Approach, Randalls Road, Leatherhead, Surrey, KT22 7TE (Tel: 01372 363666, Fax: 01372 3638333).

SUPER HEARING AID

I suppose that this project could be regarded as a hearing aid for those who do not have a hearing impediment. In other words, it is designed to provide someone who has normal hearing with super-human hearing. Probably the main users of equipment of this type are nature lovers, who use it to enable them to hear distant bird songs more clearly. A unit of this type can also be used to eavesdrop on any distant animals, insects in the undergrowth, etc.

The unit can be constructed as a self-contained device complete with built-in microphone. However, after a fair amount of experimentation with devices of this type I would not recommend this approach. To my ears at any rate, results are much better using an external microphone that should be as directional as possible. Particularly if you have very good hearing, the advantage of a unit of this type lies largely in the directional quality of the microphone. Human hearing is to a large extent omni-directional, which means that in addition to the required bird song (or whatever) you are often forced to listen to numerous other sounds as well. Using a highly directional microphone aimed in the appropriate direction you can pick out the required sound while to a substantial extent cutting out most other sounds.

Figure 31 shows the block diagram for the hearing aid. The microphone feeds into a low noise preamplifier. It is important that this stage has an extremely low noise level as the amplified sounds would otherwise be swamped by the background "hiss" of the amplifier. The next stage is a highpass

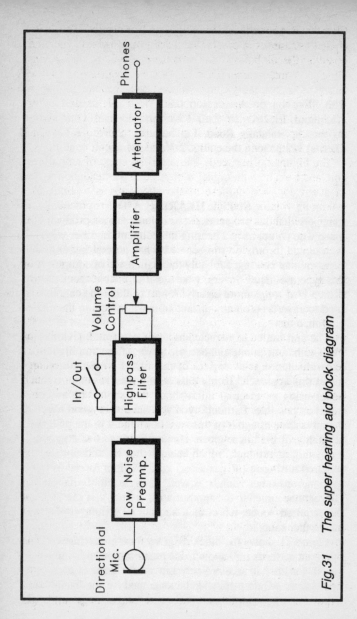

Fig.31   The super hearing aid block diagram

filter that can be switched in or bypassed, as desired. This is included as a means of combatting background noises generated by either the wind blowing across the microphone, or by handling the microphone. Due to the high sensitivity of the circuit it is inevitably quite vulnerable to general problems with vibration of the microphone. Wind-shields and other mechanical methods are the most effective way of counteracting this type of thing, but it is still useful to have the lowpass filtering when using the equipment under difficult conditions.

The highpass filter feeds into a further stage of amplification, and from here the signal is coupled to the headphones via an attenuator. The purpose of the attenuator is to limit the maximum volume from the headphones. There is potentially a major problem with even moderately loud sounds producing a deafening volume level from the headphones. One way of overcoming the problem would be to have some form of automatic volume control, but I found that this method was not too satisfactory in practice. There is a tendency for vibration of the microphone and extraneous sounds to hold down the gain of the circuit for a substantial percentage of the time.

I found that results were much better if the output of the unit was simply limited to a level that does not permit high volume levels to be produced from the headphones. The amplifier will be overloaded and will clip the output signal when loud sounds are present, giving a high distortion level on the output signal. However, as soon as a loud sound has ceased, the unit will operate normally again. An automatic gain control system can not have this instant recovery once a loud sound has stopped, and tends to be less satisfactory in use. I also found the large variations in gain produced by an automatic volume control gave rather confusing results.

The Circuit
Figure 32 shows the full circuit diagram for the super hearing aid project. The input stage is an inverting mode amplifier based on IC1. This is a TLE2037CP operational amplifier, and this is an ultra low noise and distortion type specifically designed for use in audio preamplifier circuits. It therefore provides an excellent signal to noise ratio, even though the output from the microphone will often be only a few tens of

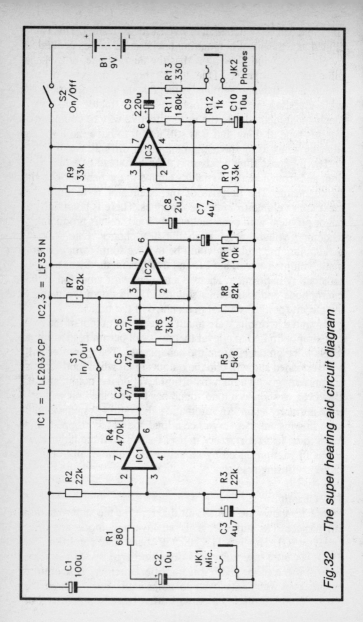

Fig.32 The super hearing aid circuit diagram

76

microvolts. R1 and R4 set the input impedance of the circuit at about 680R, and the closed loop voltage gain of IC1 at almost 700 times. An input impedance of 680R is a good match for low impedance dynamic microphones, and electret types having a built-in source follower preamplifier (but no step-up transformer). I prefer electret microphones, but quite good results can be obtained using even an inexpensive dynamic microphone of the type used with cassette recorders.

The highpass filter is a straightforward third order (18db per octave) type based on IC2. Its cutoff frequency is approximately 400Hz. This is low enough to ensure that most wildlife sounds are largely left intact, but high enough to give good attenuation of low frequency "clunks" and wind noise. The output of IC2 is fed to volume control VR1, and from here the signal is coupled to the input of the second amplifier. This is a non-inverting mode amplifier based on IC3. It has a closed loop voltage gain of about 180 times, giving the circuit an overall voltage gain of about 125,000 times. This is high enough to give excellent sensitivity with practically any low impedance dynamic or electret microphone. In fact the voltage gain might be excessive with some microphones, and it would then be advisable to reduce the gain of the circuit by reducing R4 to a value of about 220k.

Attenuation at the output is provided by R13. The specified value of 330R should give good results, but the ideal value obviously depends on the sensitivity of the headphones used. Also, some users will no doubt prefer higher maximum volume levels than others. You may therefore prefer to use a higher value in order to give reduced maximum volume, or a lower level to give increased maximum volume. The unit should be used with medium impedance headphones of the type sold as replacements for use with personal stereo units. It is preferable to use the "inner ear" type since these seem to be largely immune to problems with acoustic feedback. The two earpieces should be wired in series.

The current consumption from the PP3 size battery is about 5 to 6 milliamps. The voltage gain of this circuit is very high, which makes the component layout rather more critical than normal. The input and output of the circuit are out-of-phase, but a careless layout could still lead to severe instability. Keep the input and output wiring well separated, and use screened cable to carry the connection from JK1 to the circuit board.

Results are to a large extent dependent on the particular microphone used. Even a cheap low impedance dynamic microphone should provide quite good results. It should be possible to increase the directivity of a cheap microphone by using a tube in front of the microphone. In order to be effective though, the inside of the tube must be covered with some form of sound absorbing material (a soft foam material, cotton wool, etc.). Probably the best form of microphone for this application is a highly directional type as used with camcorders and professional video systems. Some of these have a "zoom" facility, and a microphone of this type should obviously be set fully to the "tele" position. The drawback of these highly directional microphones is their price. Using such a microphone is likely to double or treble the cost of the unit.

Components for Super Hearing Aid (Fig. 32)

Resistors (all 0.25 watt 5% carbon film)

R1	680R
R2	22k
R3	22k
R4	470k
R5	5k6
R6	3k3
R7	82k
R8	82k
R9	33k
R10	33k
R11	180k
R12	1k
R13	330R (see text)

Potentiometer

VR1	10k log carbon

Capacitors

C1	100μ 10V elect
C2	10μ 25V elect

C3	4µ7 50V elect
C4	47n polyester
C5	47n polyester
C6	47n polyester
C7	4µ7 50V elect
C8	2µ2 50V elect
C9	220µ 10V elect
C10	10µ 25V elect

Semiconductors

IC1	TLE2037CP
IC2	LF351N
IC3	LF351N

Miscellaneous

JK1	3.5mm jack socket
JK2	3.5mm jack socket
S1	SPST min toggle
S2	SPST min toggle
B1	9 volt (PP3 size)
	Case
	Circuit board
	Control knob
	Battery connector
	8 pin DIL IC holder (3 off)
	Medium impedance headphones (inner ear personal stereo type)
	Low impedance unidirectional dynamic or electret microphone (see text)
	Wire, solder, etc.

ECHO SOUNDER

No doubt most readers will be familiar with the basic principle of echo sounding on boats and ships. A brief high frequency sound is transmitted towards the sea bed by a transducer fitted on the underside of the hull. The equipment then "listens" for echoes of this signal burst, using either the transmitter transducer or a second transducer on the underside of the hull. The echo information is usually displayed on a c.r.t. or printed out via a chart recorder. The sophistication of the display varies considerably, but the basic idea is that a "blip" will be registered if any object reflects back the signal. The greater the depth of the detected object, the further down the display or chart the corresponding "blip" will appear.

The original echo sounders would only detect very large objects, such as the seabed or large wrecks. Modern instruments are much more sensitive, and can detect shoals of fish, or even the larger individual fish. The idea behind this project was to produce an echo sounder for use in air rather than water, to provide the user with a crude form of night-time vision. A sort of basic equivalent to a bat's echo location system in fact. An echo sounder of this type would presumably work in thick fog as well, although I have not been able to try out the prototype under these conditions.

So-called ultrasonic tape measures have been around for many years, and there have been several constructional projects for these published in the past. These use the echo-sounder principle, but simply measure the time taken for the first echo to be received, and then convert this into a displayed distance. This application requires a slightly different approach, with a display that indicates the approximate distance of not just the first echo received, but any subsequent echoes as well.

My original experiments used a low frequency pulse generator to produce a periodic burst of ultrasonic sound via a gated oscillator and an ultrasonic transducer. The receiving section consisted of a second ultrasonic transducer, a high gain amplifier, and an oscilloscope to monitor the output of the amplifier. The oscilloscope's triggered sweep facility was operated by the pulse generator at the transmitter, and was triggered by its falling edge (i.e. the sweep started as the burst of ultrasonic sound ceased).

This set up was found to work quite well, with (say) a chair in front of a wall producing an initial "blip" from the chair, and a later "blip" from the wall. The height of the oscilloscope display indicated the relative strengths of the echoes, with the more solid and substantial wall producing a stronger signal than the chair, even though the wall was further away. Producing a reasonably simple and self contained version of this set up proved to be slightly more difficult than I had anticipated. The original idea was to have a display consisting of ten bargraphs with each bargraph having ten LEDs. Each bargraph would represent a different range, and would indicate the relative strength of any echoes received at that range.

This system is no doubt perfectly feasible, but it soon became apparent that it would produce a final unit that was too costly and complex to be a practical proposition for this book. The final unit is therefore a somewhat simplified version of the original idea, with a row of ten LEDs representing distances of around 0.5 to 5 metres in 0.5 metre increments. The relative strength of a received echo is indicated by the brightness of the corresponding LED. This gives what is admittedly quite a crude display, but it is nevertheless quite effective in use.

System Operation
The block diagram of Figure 33 shows the basic arrangement used for the echo sounder. The transmitter section is much the same as in the test set up, with a clock oscillator generating a series of brief pulses that switch on a high frequency (40kHz) oscillator. This in turn drives the transmitting transducer which therefore generates short bursts of ultrasonic sound at regular intervals. The receiver section consists of a second ultrasonic transducer feeding into a two stage high gain amplifier. The amplified signal is rectified and fed to a d.c. amplifier.

The remaining stages are the display and its associated control logic. A second gated oscillator is controlled by the clock oscillator via an inverter. This second oscillator is therefore brought into action when the burst of ultrasonic sound ceases. It feeds the clock input of the display driver, which is a one of ten decoder/driver. Initially LED 1 is switched on, but on receiving the first clock cycle LED 2 is switched on and LED 1 is switched off. On the next clock cycle LED 3 is switched on and LED 2 is switched off. This general train of events continues until LED 10 is switched on and LED 9 is switched off. On the next clock cycle LED 10 would be switched off and LED 1 would be turned on again, but the clock oscillator resets the display and cuts off the second gated oscillator just before this happens.

This gives the required basic action, with each burst of

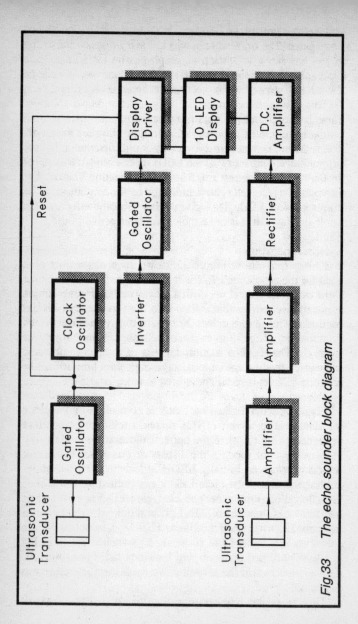

Fig.33   The echo sounder block diagram

ultrasonic sound being followed by the ten LEDs being activated in sequence. Of course, the LEDs are referenced to the output of the d.c. amplifier, and not to earth. Consequently, a LED will not necessarily be switched on when its output goes high. It will only be switched on if an echo has been received, and the output transistor of the d.c. amplifier is switched on. The stronger the echo, the stronger this output transistor will conduct, and the brighter the LED. Sound travels at approximately 1 metre every 3 milliseconds, and the second gated oscillator has a clock period of about 3 milliseconds. This gives the 0.5 metre increments from the display (bearing in mind that the sound has to travel one metre in order to produce an echo from an object 0.5 metres in front of the transducers).

The Circuit
The circuit diagram for the echo sounder appears in Figures 34 to 36. Figure 34 shows the transmitter section of the unit, plus part of the control logic. IC2 is a 555 timer which is used as a gated oscillator that generates the ultrasonic tone. The circuit uses ordinary ultrasonic transducers of the type used in remote control systems and burglar alarms. These have peak efficiency at 40kHz, and VR2 must therefore be set for an output frequency of 40kHz. The transducers are piezo-electric devices, and consequently there is no need for a d.c. blocking capacitor between IC2 and LS1. The d.c. resistance of LS1 is many megohms.

IC1 is another 555 timer, and it is used as an astable (oscillator). The output of IC1 drives a relatively high load impedance, and it is therefore perfectly acceptable to use a low power version of the 555. This helps to minimise the current consumption of the circuit. D1 modifies the normal charge/discharge cycle of the circuit so that R2 effectively becomes the only charge resistance, and the series resistance of R1 and VR1 provides the discharge resistance. This gives the required output waveform having a series of brief positive pulses. These pulses are used as the gate signal for IC2, and each one results in a short burst of ultrasonic tone from LS1. VR1 is adjusted to give the correct interval between the bursts of ultrasonic sound. TR1 provides an inverted version of IC1's output signal. This is used to control the oscillator in the display circuit.

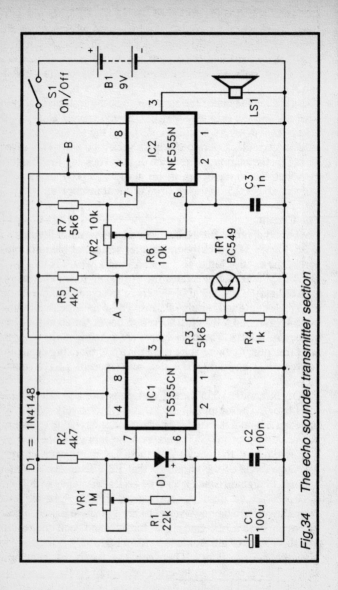

Fig.34   The echo sounder transmitter section

84

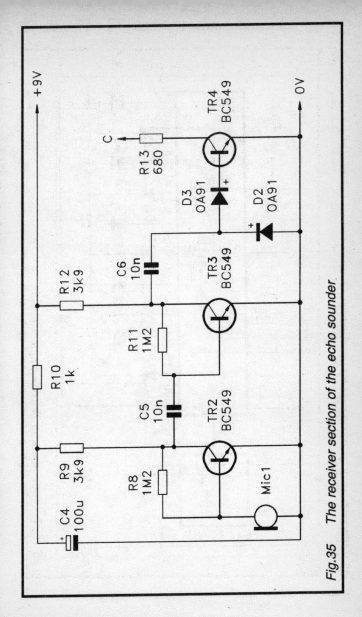

Fig.35   The receiver section of the echo sounder.

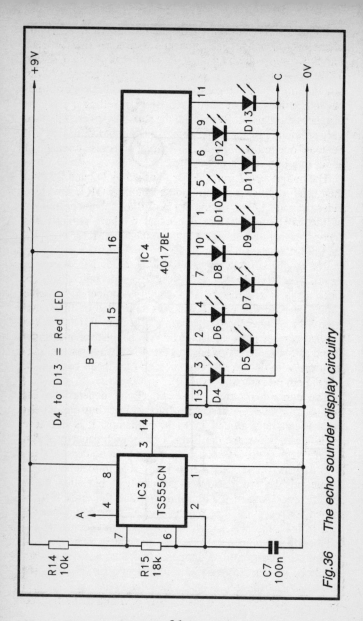

Fig.36   The echo sounder display circuitry

86

Figure 35 shows the circuit diagram for the receiver section of the echo sounder. The ultrasonic transducer (Mic1) feeds into a two stage common emitter amplifier based on TR2 and TR3. These provide well over 80dB of voltage gain at 40kHz, but this high level of gain is essential as ultrasonic sounds become seriously attenuated even when travelling quite short distances through air. Even when the soundwaves are reflected very efficiently by the target object, the output from Mic1 will be under one millivolt r.m.s. if the target object is at a range of about four or five metres.

The output signal from TR3 is rectified by D2 and D3, and then used to drive common emitter amplifier TR4. This provides the path to earth for the display LEDs, and the brightness of the LEDS is therefore dependent on how strongly the echoed signal drives TR4 into conduction. R13 provides current limiting for the display LEDs.

The display circuitry appears in Figure 36. The display is driven by IC4, which is a CMOS one of ten decoder/driver. Its clock signal is provided by IC3, which is another 555 astable circuit. It is a gated astable which is controlled by the signal from TR1 (Figure 34). The direct output from IC1 is used to provide a reset pulse to IC4 while each pulse of ultrasonic sound is transmitted. This ensures that IC4 always starts counting from zero once each burst of sound has been completed, and the circuit enters its "listening" mode.

The current consumption of the circuit depends on the number of LEDs that are active at the time, but the current drain is normally around 15 to 20 milliamps. It is therefore advisable to power the unit from a fairly high capacity 9 volt battery, such as six HP7 size cells in a plastic holder.

Ultrasonic transducers are normally sold in matched pairs. Sometimes the two transducers are identical, but often one is specifically designed for transmission, and the other is optimisied for reception. The retailer's catalogue should make it clear if this is the case, and should also explain which is which. Although the unit does not simultaneously transmit and "listen", I would still recommend that the two transducers should be mounted at least 75 millimetres apart. None of the ultrasonic transducers I have used have had any built-in mounting bracket, and the easiest way of fixing them in place is to use an epoxy adhesive. Most of these transducers have one terminal connected to the metal case. This terminal should be the one that connects to the 0 volt supply rail.

Adjustment and Use

It is probably easiest to adjust VR1 if a temporary shorting link is first placed across the collector and emitter leads of TR4 so that all the display LEDs can be switched on at full brightness. The number of LEDs that actually switch on is controlled by VR1. This preset is set just high enough in value to cause all ten LEDs to light up, with the final LED in the display lighting up at something close to the brightness of the other LEDs. The display will flicker slightly because it is refreshed only about 25 to 30 times per second. The time taken for the bursts of sound to be echoed by objects at a range of about 5 metres or so precludes the use of a higher refresh rate.

VR2 could be set for an output frequency of 40kHz with the aid of a frequency meter. However, the transducers will probably not provide peak efficiency at precisely 40kHz. The only way of finding the optimum setting for VR2 is to use a bit of trial and error. Any setting that provides correct operation with all the LEDs brought into action is satisfactory.

There is a slight flaw in the design since objects more than about 5 metres away could produce echoes that would operate LEDs one and two on the next display cycle. In practice this does not seem to be a major problem, since objects much more than about 5 metres from the unit are unlikely to produce strong enough echoes to light a LED reasonably brightly. As the first two LEDs represent distances of around 0.5 and 1 metre they are not particularly useful anyway, and they could simply be omitted.

Results using the unit are quite interesting, and are remarkably good when one takes into account the extreme simplicity of the unit. I sometimes found that the display was rather confusing if the unit was used indoors, particularly if it was used in small rooms. The problem seems to be due to the bursts of sound being echoed around the room, giving a jumble of echoes back at the receiver section of the unit. This can sometimes result in practically all the LEDs switching on, even if there is a large clear area in front of the unit.

When used out-of-doors, or indoors in a reasonably large room, results seem to be far better. For example, by scanning the unit slowly from side to side I found that the display clearly showed a strong echo from a fence about 4.5 metres away, and a slightly closer but weaker echo from a hedge just in front of the fence. The unit is quite directional, and it is easy to home-in on a target once it has been located.

Components for Echo Sounder (Figs 34, 35, and 36)

Resistors (all 0.25 watt 5% carbon film)
R1	22k
R2	4k7
R3	5k6
R4	1k
R5	4k7
R6	10k
R7	5k6
R8	1M2
R9	3k9
R10	1k
R11	1M2
R12	3k9
R13	680R
R14	10k
R15	18k

Potentiometers
VR1	1M min preset
VR2	10k min preset

Capacitors
C1	100μ 10V elect
C2	100n polyester
C3	1n polyester
C4	100μ 10V elect
C5	10n polyester
C6	10n polyester
C7	100n polyester

Semiconductors

IC1	TS555CN or similar
IC2	NE555N
IC3	TS555CN or similar
IC4	4017BE
TR1 to TR4	BC549 (4 off)
D1	1N4148
D2	OA91
D3	OA91
D4 to D13	High brightness Red panel LEDs

Miscellaneous

B1	9 volt (6 × HP7 size cells in holder)
S1	SPST min toggle
Mic1	40kHz ultrasonic transducer
LS1	40kHz ultrasonic transducer
	Case
	Circuit board
	Battery connector (PP3 type)
	8 pin DIL IC holder (3 off)
	14 pin DIL IC holder
	Wire, solder, etc.

LED STROBOSCOPE

Those readers who are old enough to remember the early LEDs of the 1970s will no doubt also remember their very low light output levels. Except in very dim conditions it was often difficult to see whether they were switched on or off! The efficiency of LEDs has steadily increased over the years, and even the cheaper LEDs now offer relatively high output levels. In fact the best of modern ultra-bright LEDs are about a thousand times brighter than the early types. The brightness of the highest output types is quite surprising, and a current of 20 milliamps is sufficient to produce a torch-like beam. The light output falls well short of that from the average torch, but in a room at normal brightness a noticeable red patch can be produced on a wall a metre or two from the LED.

Although at one time visible light LEDs were of little use for anything other than indicator lights, the vastly higher outputs of modern ultra-bright types starts to open up other possibilities. Those readers who studied physics at school will probably remember experiments using a stroboscope (a flashing light) to "freeze" the movement of machinery. The flashing of the stroboscope is carefully adjusted so that it is accurately synchronised with the movement of the machinery. Therefore, each time the stroboscope flashes, the machinery is in the same position, and it seems to be stationary.

More interestingly, if the stroboscope is set fractionally too low in frequency, the machinery will have moved on slightly each time the light flashes. This makes the mechanism appear to move and operate normally, but in slow motion. Setting the stroboscope slightly too high in frequency has much the same effect, but the machinery seems to run backwards!

LEDs are capable of the relatively high switching speeds needed for a stroboscope, but it is only fair to point out that the light output from even the best of modern LEDs when pulsed at high currents is far less than the light output from even a small flashtube. A LED stroboscope will certainly work, but it is only usable with small pieces of machinery under subdued lighting. On the plus side, the cost of most ultra-bright LEDs is quite small (under a pound), and no complex or expensive driver circuitry is required. This makes it possible to experiment with LED stroboscopes at minimal cost.

The Circuit

On the face of it, all that is required is an oscillator driving an ultra-bright LED. In practice the circuit must meet some stringent requirements if it is to provide good results. One obvious requirement is that the average LED current must be reasonably high. Most LEDs are designed to operate at currents of up to at least 20 milliamps, and the LED should therefore be driven at a current that is not far short of this figure.

Another important factor is that the flashes from the LED must be quite short. A few practical experiments suggest that the LED must be driven by a signal having a mark-space ratio of at least 100 to 1 if the "frozen" images are to be reasonably sharp. Longer flashes result in the machinery moving significantly during each flash, giving a very blurred image. A problem that arises with such a high mark-space ratio is that

LED must be pulsed at a very high current in order to produce a reasonably high average LED current. In fact a LED current of about 2 amps is needed in order to give an average current of 20 milliamps. Fortunately, LEDs are able to withstand such high currents provided the current is applied only very briefly, and the average LED current is kept within the LED's normal range of continuous operating currents.

Producing an oscillator that has a mark-space ratio of about 100 to 1 is easy enough, but maintaining that mark-space ratio with reasonable accuracy over a wide frequency range is more difficult. Figure 37 shows the circuit that I finally devised, and this is based on two 555 timers. IC1 is a low power 555 used in the astable mode. Its output frequency can be varied from about 30Hz with VR1a at maximum resistance to 560Hz with VR1a at minimum resistance. In terms of r.p.m. this represents a range of about 1800 to 33,600.

The output waveform from IC1 is not of great importance since it is IC2 that controls the output waveform. This is a standard 555 used in the monostable mode. It is triggered on the negative edge of IC1's output signal due to the loose coupling via C3. The duration of IC2's output pulses is controlled by VR1b, and varies from approximately 0.25 milliseconds at maximum resistance to 11.3 microseconds at minimum resistance. This gives some variation in the mark-space ratio of the output signal, but not enough to be of practical significance. The mark-space ratio is always comfortably in excess of 100 to 1.

TR1 simply acts as an emitter follower buffer stage which drives the LED at a suitably high current. I would recommend the use of a standard 555 for IC2 as this ensures a low drive impedance to TR1, which should in turn ensure that TR1 drives the LED at an "on" current of about 2 amps. Even with such a high drive current, the average LED current will still be a little under 20 milliamps. The total current consumption of the circuit is nearer 30 milliamps, necessitating the use of a fairly high capacity 9 volt battery (e.g. six HP7 size cells in a plastic holder).

In Use
The unit should work well using any ultra-bright LED for D1.

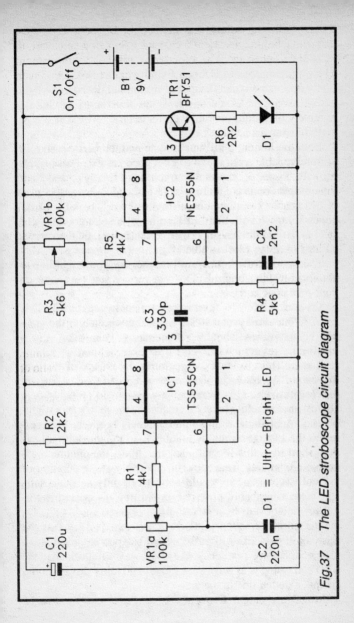

Fig.37   The LED stroboscope circuit diagram

Exactly what constitutes an ultra-bright LED these days is debatable, but in this case it means a LED having an output of at least 1cd (1000mcd) at a forward current of 20 milliamps. The highest output LED I could find was the RS/Electromail type which has a typical output of some 14cd. Its beam of light is less even than would be ideal, but it certainly provides a relatively high light output level. Its main drawback is a high price of over ten pounds.

Both the Maplin 8 millimetre type and the Electrovalue 10 millimetre LED were found to give good results. These LEDs provide beams of reasonably even light intensity, and their light output levels are quite high (1.6cd and 2–3cd respectively). At around one pound each they will not "break the bank" either. Some 5 millimetre LEDs also give quite good results, such as the Maplin "hyper-bright" LED (3.5cd). Of the various LEDs I tried the Electrovalue 10 millimetre device gave what I consider to be the best overall results, but you might like to obtain a few ultra-bright LEDs from various sources and reach your own conclusions.

The unit is likely to be more convenient in use if the LED is fitted into a small probe style case and connected to the main unit via a twin lead about 0.5 metres long. This makes it very much easier to get the LED into a suitable position.

It is possible to shift the operating frequency of the unit downwards by changing the values of C2 and C4 to 470n and 4n7 respectively. This would give what would probably be a slightly more useful operating frequency range, but it is slightly risky. A LED can only be pulsed safely at a very high current if the average current is suitably low, and the pulse time is very short. It is this second point that limits the minimum acceptable operating frequency. In practice a pulse duration of 0.5 milliseconds or so would almost certainly be quite safe, and there is probably little risk in shifting the operating frequency downwards by a factor of two or three.

The normal frequency range of the unit is such that the flashing of the LED will probably not be apparent, even at the lowest operating frequency. An easy way to check that the LED is flashing is to wave the LED around fairly fast. It should "paint" a dotted line in the air.

In use the output frequency of the stroboscope must be

accurately matched to the operating frequency of the machinery. This is just a matter of slowly varying the setting of VR1 until the desired effect is obtained. Note that a stationary view of the machinery will be obtained if the stroboscope only flashes on every second, third, etc., cycle of the machinery. However, this will not give optimum results as a relatively blurred view will be obtained. Use the highest frequency that gives the desired result. If the flash rate is several times that of the machinery's operating frequency a sort of multiple "frozen" view will be obtained. This could sometimes be quite useful, but in most cases it will simply produce rather confusing results.

Of course, when operating near any piece of machinery, even if it is not large and very powerful machinery, due care should be taken. Always keep a reasonable distance away from moving parts. Ultra-bright LEDs have reasonably narrow angles of "view", so there is no need to use the unit at point-blank range.

Components for LED Stroboscope (Fig. 37)

Resistors (all 0.25 watt 5% carbon film)
R1	4k7
R2	2k2
R3	5k6
R4	5k6
R5	4k7
R6	2R2

Potentiometer
VR1	100k lin carbon dual gang

Capacitors
C1	220µ 10V elect
C2	220n polyester
C3	330p polystyrene
C4	2n2 polyester

Semiconductors
IC1	TS555CN or similar
IC2	NE555N
D1	Ultra-bright LED (see text)

B1   9 volt (6 × HP7 size cells in holder)
S1   SPST min toggle
              Case
              Probe style case for D1
              Circuit board
              Battery connector (PP3 type)
              8 pin DIL IC holder (2 off)
              Control knob
              Wire, solder, etc.

LONG RANGE REMOTE CONTROL

Probably most readers are familiar with infra-red remote control systems, since these now seem to be supplied as standard with many video recorders, television sets, and pieces of audio equipment. Although these systems operate using invisible infra-red "light", it is not essential to use infra-red. Systems based on red LEDs and ordinary phototransistors can work perfectly well, and an obvious use for an ultra-bright LED is in a relatively long range remote control system. Ordinary infra-red remote control systems normally operate at ranges of up to 5 metres, but a range of two or three times this figure should be possible using ultra-bright LEDs.

The circuits of Figures 38 and 39 are respectively for a simple remote control transmitter and a matching receiver. These provide simple on/off switching, with the relay at the receiver being operated when the push-button switch at the transmitter is operated. The system could be used as a remote means of triggering a camera that has provision for an electric release, or some equally straightforward application. The circuits are "borrowed" from the book "*Practical Opto-Electronic Projects*" (BP349), from the same publisher and author as this book. The only difference is that the infra-red LED at the output of the original transmitter circuit has been replaced by an ultra-bright red LED.

The transmitter circuit is basically just a 555 astable operating at a frequency of about 4.5kHz. Its virtually squarewave output drives LED D1 via emitter follower stage TR1 and current limiter R3. The latter sets the average LED current at

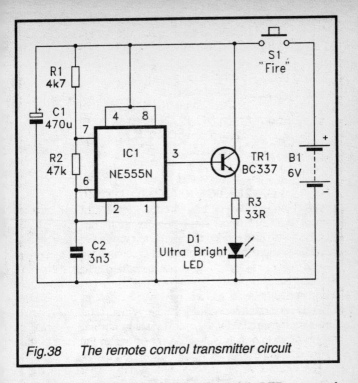

Fig.38   The remote control transmitter circuit

approximately 50 milliamps. Some ultra-bright LEDs are rated to take an operating current of 50 milliamps, but others are limited to a maximum continuous current of 20 or 30 milliamps. In practice the transmitter would normally only be operated in short and infrequent bursts, which would not put D1 at much risk. However, if you do not wish to take any risks, increase the value of R3 to 82R for an average current of 20 milliamps, or 56R for an effective LED current of 30 milliamps.

The receiver circuit has a phototransistor (TR1) as the light detector. Although a BPX25 is specified for TR1, the circuit will work properly using practically any phototransistor that operates in the visible light part of the spectrum. I found that phototransistors of the type which have a 5 millimetre LED style encapsulation worked very well, and they are also relatively cheap. Obviously the phototransistor should not be an

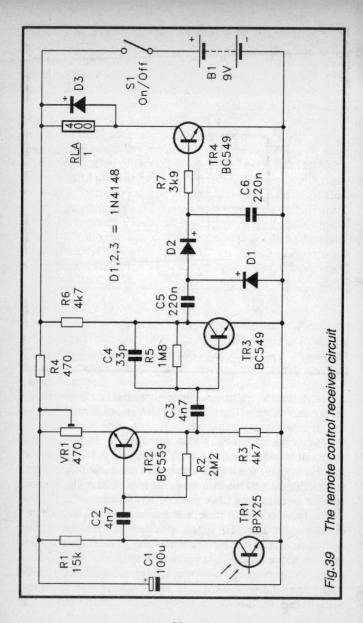

Fig.39   The remote control receiver circuit

infra-red type having a built-in "daylight" filter, as the filter would largely block the red light from the transmitter. No connection is made to the base terminal of the transistor, and this leadout is actually absent on many modern phototransistors. If the base lead is present, and there are any problems with stray pick up here, it should be wired to the 0 volt supply rail.

The output from TR1 is coupled to a two stage common emitter amplifier which can provide more than 80dB of voltage gain. This level of voltage gain might prove to be excessive, with the noise from TR1 being sufficient to hold the circuit in the active state. To avoid this the gain of the amplifier must be backed-off to a level that permits proper operation of the system. This is achieved by adjusting VR1 for increased resistance. With VR1 at minimum resistance there is no local negative feedback applied to TR2, and it operates at its full voltage gain of well over 40dB. Adjusting VR1 higher in value introduces an increasing amount of local negative feedback to TR2, resulting in a voltage gain of only about 20dB with VR1 at maximum resistance.

The values of coupling capacitors C2 and C3 have been deliberately kept low in order to reduce the sensitivity of the circuit to 100Hz "hum" from mains powered lighting. C4 introduces a small amount of high frequency roll-off which helps to avoid problems with instability. However, due to the high gain of the circuit, plus the fact that the input and output of the circuit are in-phase, due care must still be taken with the component layout if problems with instability are to be avoided.

C5 couples the output of TR3 to a simple half-wave rectifier and smoothing circuit based on D1 and D2. In the absence of a signal from the transmitter the positive d.c. output signal from this circuit is insufficient to bias TR4 into conduction. When a suitably strong signal is received from the transmitter TR4 is biased hard into conduction, and the relay coil in its collector circuit is activated. D3 is the usual protection diode which suppresses the high reverse voltage that would otherwise be generated across the relay as it switched off.

The relay can be any type which has a coil resistance of about 200 ohms or more, and suitable contacts for your particular application, provided it will operate reliably from a little under 9 volts. Most 12 volt relays will actually work perfectly well on a supply of about 8 volts, but if necessary the unit can be powered from a 12 volt battery (e.g. eight HP7 size cells in a holder instead of six HP7 size cells). The current consumption of the circuit is only a few milliamps under standby conditions, but is likely to be around 30 to 40 milliamps (depending on the relay's coil resistance) when in the "on" state.

Results

Using the original infra-red remote control circuit it was possible to obtain a maximum operating range of about 7 metres. In fact a somewhat greater range could be obtained if VR1 was set just below the point at which the relay was activated, but there are practical reasons for backing it off a little further than this. With the circuit on the verge of operating the relay there is a danger of frequent spurious triggering. Also, the standby current consumption of the circuit is relatively high. Backing off the gain slightly using VR1 gives better reliability and a lower quiescent current consumption.

A range of 7 metres was easily achieved using the prototype equipment, and this clearly represented nothing like the maximum range of the system. With any good ultra-bright LED a range of 15 metres or more can be achieved, which is quite impressive for a system that has no optics other than the built-in lenses of the LED and phototransistor. When using this system it is important to bear in mind that both the transmitter and receiver are to some extent directional, and operation over 10 metres or more is only possible if the aim of the transmitter and receiver are both reasonably accurate. The narrower the "angle of view" of the two optical devices, the greater the maximum operating range, but the more directional the system becomes.

Components for Remote Control Transmitter (Fig. 38)

Resistors (all 0.25 watt 5% carbon film)
R1   4k7
R2   47k
R3   33R (see text)

Capacitors
C1   470µ 10V elect
C2   3n3 polyester

Semiconductors
IC1   NE555N
TR1   BC337
D1   Ultra-bright LED

Miscellaneous
S1   Push to make, release to break push button
            switch
B1   6 volt (4 × HP7 size cells in holder)
            Case
            Circuit board
            Battery connector (PP3 type)
            8 pin DIL IC holder
            Wire, solder, etc.

Components for Remote Control Receiver (Fig. 39)

Resistors (all 0.25 watt 5% carbon film)
R1   15k
R2   2M2
R3   4k7
R4   470R
R5   1M8
R6   4k7
R7   3k9

Capacitors
C1   100µ 16V elect
C2   4n7 polyester
C3   4n7 polyester
C4   33p polystyrene
C5   220n polyester
C6   220n polyester

Semiconductors

TR1	BPX25 (see text)
TR2	BC559
TR3	BC549
TR4	BC549
D1	1N4148
D2	1N4148
D3	1N4148

Miscellaneous

S1	SPST min toggle
B1	9 volt (6 × HP7 size cells in holder)
RLA	12 volt coil having a resistance of 200R or more, and contacts to suit your application (see text)
	Case
	Circuit board
	Battery connector (PP3 type)
	Wire, solder, etc.

STRAIN GAUGE

Strain gauges are used routinely in industry, but seem to be little used in electronic designs for the amateur. I suppose that in industry there are many occasions when it is essential to measure the strain on something or other, and many new bridges, etc., are apparently monitored using numerous strain gauges at strategic points on the structure. For the amateur user there are few practical applications, if any. Nevertheless, strain gauges are interesting to experiment with, and are something that is well worth giving a try if you have never tried one before.

In essence a strain gauge is very simple indeed. Figure 40 shows the basic arrangement used in a strain gauge sensor. A small piece of thin plastic has a zig-zag of thin metal deposited on its surface. A leadout wire is connected to each end of this thin metal track. The resistance through the track is quite low, but due to the thinness of the track it is not a matter of milliohms. The resistance through a strain gauge sensor is typically about 100 ohms.

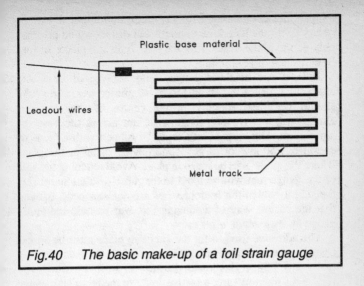

Fig.40   The basic make-up of a foil strain gauge

This simple arrangement may not seem to provide the desired effect, but it will do so provided it is very securely glued to the surface of the object that is being monitored. If the object is flexed in one direction the strain gauge is stretched slightly, and the track is lengthened. This gives what is effectively a longer and thinner track, and the resistance through the track therefore increases. If the object is flexed in the opposite direction the track is compressed, giving what is effectively a shorter but wider track. Accordingly, the track resistance falls. The variation in resistance is not very great, and is normally well under 1% even if the monitored object is quite severely distorted. In use a large amount of amplification is normally needed in order to obtain a usable voltage swing from a strain gauge.

Practical Gauges
As far as I can ascertain, the only source of strain gauges open to amateur users is RS/Electromail. They stock several types, but for the experimenter the 5 millimetre foil type is probably the best choice. These are available in two versions. One is temperature compensated for use with steel, and the other is

temperature compensated for use with aluminium. I experimented with the aluminium variety, but results would presumably be much the same using the steel type and pieces of thin steel instead of aluminium.

I fixed one of these gauges onto a piece of 18 s.w.g. aluminium measuring about 150 by 40 millimetres. The gauge should be fitted roughly in the centre of the sheet of aluminium, and running lengthwise, not across the piece of aluminium. The aluminium should be rubbed with a piece of cotton or cottonwool to get it thoroughly clean at the place where the gauge will be glued in place. Avoid touching the side of the gauge that will be fixed to the piece of aluminium (i.e. the side to which the leadout wires are not attached). I found that the easiest way of achieving this was to hold the strain gauge by its leadout wires only.

The adhesive used to fix the gauge in place must be an extremely powerful type, but this is no problem these days as virtually any "Superglue" will do the job well. Provided you follow the manufacturer's instructions "to the letter" the gauge should be securely attached to the piece of aluminium, and should give good results. Allow adequate time for the adhesive to set before using the strain gauge in any experiments. Bear in mind that many quick setting adhesives take about 24 hours to achieve their absolute maximum bonding strength.

Two minute self adhesive printed circuit boards are provided with each strain gauge. These are used to provide strain relief, and they are stuck on the sheet of aluminium about 20 millimetres away from the gauge. Each little circuit board has two interconnected copper pads. One pad of each board connects to a leadout wire of the strain gauge, and the remaining two pads connect to the strain gauge amplifier via an insulated lead. Make sure that the strain gauge's leadout wires (which are not insulated) do not short circuit to the piece of aluminium.

The Circuit

Special strain gauge amplifier integrated circuits are available, but for experimental purposes a simple amplifier of the type shown in Figure 41 will suffice. Note though, that for good results IC1 must be a type intended for precision d.c.

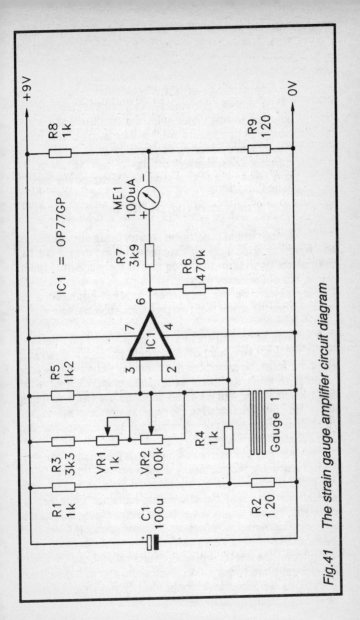

Fig.41   The strain gauge amplifier circuit diagram

105

applications. The circuit is basically just a non-inverting mode amplifier having a voltage gain of about 430 times. The input voltage is produced by a potentiometer which has R3, R5, VR1, and VR2 as one element, and the strain gauge as the other. The output voltage of IC1 is monitored by a voltmeter based on ME1, and this is connected in a simple bridge circuit. VR1 is adjusted so that under quiescent conditions the meter reads something close to zero. VR2 is then used to "fine tune" the meter to produce a reading of precisely zero.

The current consumption of the circuit is about 25 milliamps. I powered it from a stabilised bench power supply, but reasonably good results should be obtained using a fairly high capacity 9 volt battery (e.g. six HP7 size cells in a plastic holder).

The obvious initial experiment is to try using this equipment as a weighing scale. I placed a couple of small boxes about 100 millimetres or so apart, and then placed the piece of aluminium on top of the boxes with the strain gauge on the underside. Placing objects on the aluminium "bridge" produced a response from the meter, but two problems soon became apparent.

The more serious of these was a pronounced non-linearity in the scaling. Quite light objects would produce a significant response from the meter, but a substantial weight was needed in order to bring the meter to something approaching a full scale reading. The unit could no doubt be used as a weighing scale, but only by calibrating the meter against a set of weights. In practice this type of custom recalibration is time-consuming and difficult, but it is possible.

Problem number two was simply that the aluminium sheet lacked elasticity. Placing heavy objects on the "bridge" flexed the piece of aluminium by a substantial amount, but once the weight was removed the aluminium remained quite heavily distorted. This in turn resulted in the meter failing to return to a reading of zero. On reflection, it would probably have been better to experiment with a piece of thin steel (about 20 or 22 s.w.g.), plus the steel compensated versions of the strain gauge. Steel is far more springy than aluminium, and would be better suited to a weighing scale application. Strain gauges are certainly interesting to experiment with, and I will certainly make further attempts at perfecting a strain gauge weighing scale.

Components for Strain Gauge Amplifier (Fig. 41)

Resistors (all 0.25 watt 1% metal film)

R1	1k
R2	120R
R3	3k3
R4	1k
R5	1k2
R6	470k
R7	3k9
R8	1k
R9	120R

Potentiometers

VR1	1k lin carbon
VR2	100k lin carbon

Capacitor

C1	100µ 10V elect

Semiconductor

IC1	OP77GP, OPA177GP, or similar

Miscellaneous

ME1	100µA moving coil panel meter
	Case
	Circuit board
	5 millimetre strain gauge (see text)
	18 s.w.g. aluminium, 150 × 40 millimetres
	8 pin DIL IC holder
	Wire, solder, etc.

NOISE CANCELLING

The modern world seems to be an increasingly noisy place, and it is not really surprising that there is increasing interest in methods of combating noise pollution. Most methods of combating noise are purely mechanical, but it is also possible to reduce noise using electronic noise cancelling equipment. Indeed, some systems of this type have been produced commercially, but have mainly been aimed at specialist markets. In particular, they have mainly been used to combat vehicle noise of various types.

Electronic noise cancelling provides an interesting challenge for the electronics experimenter, but it has to be pointed out that it is a rather tougher proposition than we are sometimes led to believe. It is simple enough in theory, and it is basically just a matter of generating an inverted version of the sound so that the original noise and the inverted replica cancel out one another. This sort of cancelling process is commonplace in electronic circuits, and a high degree of cancelling is normally possible.

When applied to sound it is more difficult to obtain good results, mainly due to imperfections in the transducers used. It is easy enough to design electronic circuits that have flat frequency responses and no significant phase shifts over the audio band, but loudspeakers and microphones having these characteristics are rare and expensive. Using more affordable transducers compromises results, and can easily result in a system that does not work to a worthwhile degree (if at all).

Phasing

The waveforms of Figure 42 help to explain the way in which phase cancelling systems work. In (a) the top two waveforms represent the two input signals. These are identical in amplitude and are precisely in-phase. The bottom waveform is the result of mixing these two signals together so that their signal voltages are added together. As one would expect, the output signal is identical to the two input signals, but is at double their amplitude.

The waveforms of (b) are of more importance in the current context. The two input waveforms are a sinewave signal and an inverted version of that signal. The amplitudes of the two signals are identical, but they are always of the opposite polarity. Mixing them together so that the signal voltages are added therefore gives zero volts, and no output signal. Although the signals in Figure 42 are simple sinewaves, the same principles

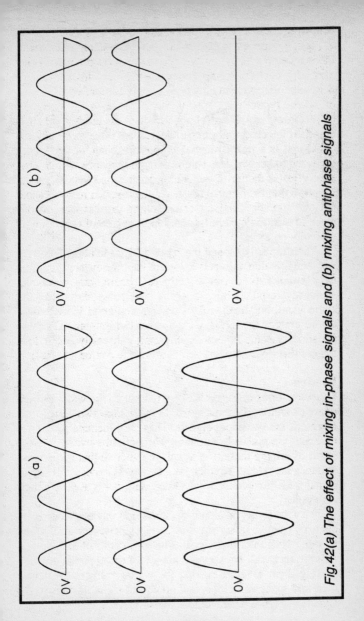

Fig.42(a) The effect of mixing in-phase signals and (b) mixing antiphase signals

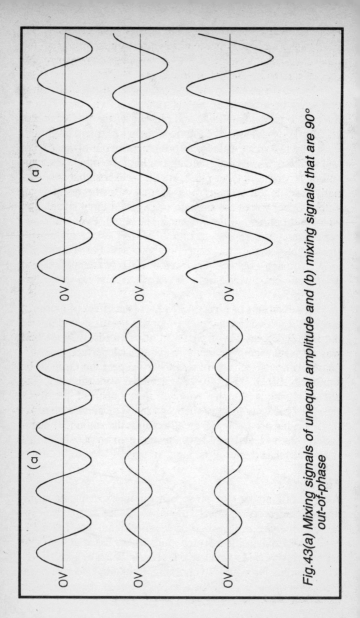

Fig.43(a) Mixing signals of unequal amplitude and (b) mixing signals that are 90° out-of-phase

110

apply no matter how complex the input signals are made. In-phase signals add together to produce a stronger version of the input signal, and identical anti-phase signals always cancel out one another to produce no output signal.

When experimenting with any phase cancelling system it is important to realise that perfect cancelling will only be obtained if both the amplitude and phasing of the two signals is correct. The waveforms of Figure 43 help to explain this point. In (a) the two input waveforms are precisely out-of-phase, but one signal is at only half the amplitude of the other. The cancelling process still takes place, but the weaker signal only partially cancels the stronger one. In this case the result is an output signal at half the strength of the main input signal, and equal in amplitude to the weaker input signal. Even quite minor mismatches in the strengths of the two signals will significantly impair the cancelling process. For example, a 10% mismatch would only give about 20dB or attenuation, and even a 1% error would limit the attenuation to no more than about 40dB.

The waveforms of Figure 43(b) show the effect of incorrect phasing. The two input waveforms have identical amplitudes, but are 90 degrees out-of-phase. In other words, they are half way between being perfectly in-phase and perfectly out-of-phase. Although you might reasonably expect the result to be similar to that in (a), it does not actually work this way. The output signal is actually stronger than either of the input signals! This demonstrates the importance of precise phasing. Poor phasing accuracy will greatly reduce the amount of attenuation achieved, and could even result in an output signal that is stronger than either of the input signals.

The Circuit
After a fair amount of noise cancelling experiments using loudspeaker based systems I failed to obtain any significant noise cancelling at all. Acoustic feedback and "howl around" is one potential problem with a loudspeaker based system, but setups which avoided feedback problems failed to give worthwhile results. No doubt it is possible to obtain effective noise cancelling using in a loudspeaker based system, but equipment using headphones seems to be a better starting point.

Headphones virtually eliminate any problems with acoustic feedback, and seem to provide much better results. Even inexpensive headphones of the "inner ear" variety seem to provide quite good results, but the more expensive types work that much better, particularly at the extremes of the audio range.

In its most basic form a noise cancelling system simply consists of two microphones feeding into a stereo preamplifier, which in turn drives the stereo headphones. A gain control must be fitted so that the amplitude of the "anti-noise" can be precisely matched to that of the direct noise. The gain must be separately adjustable for each ear if good results are to be obtained.

It is also helpful to have the option of inverted and non-inverted signals. You have to bear in mind here that the phasing of the sound from the headphones relative to the direct sound is something of an unknown quantity. Apart from other factors, it depends on which way round the leads are connected to the microphone and the earphone. The only way of determining whether or not the phasing is correct is to adopt a "suck it and see" approach, with the signal being inverted by some means if the unit makes the noise louder rather than quieter. An "invert" switch provides a quick and easy way of altering the phasing if this should prove to be necessary.

Figure 44 shows the circuit diagram for a microphone pre-amplifier that is suitable for use in a noise cancelling system. This is for one channel only, and two of these preamplifiers are needed for a practical noise cancelling system. Of course, B1 and on/off switch S2 can be common to both preamplifier circuits, and do not need to be duplicated for the second channel. Also, JK2 is a 3.5 millimetre stereo jack socket which is common to both preamplifier circuits.

The circuit itself is a simple high gain low noise preamplifier having IC1 as an inverting mode amplifier. The closed loop voltage gain of this stage is about 320 times, and its input impedance is 680 ohms. This input impedance suits any low impedance microphone, such as an electret type or a dynamic microphone which does not have a built-in step-up transformer. The choice of microphone is something that is considered in more detail in the next section of this book.

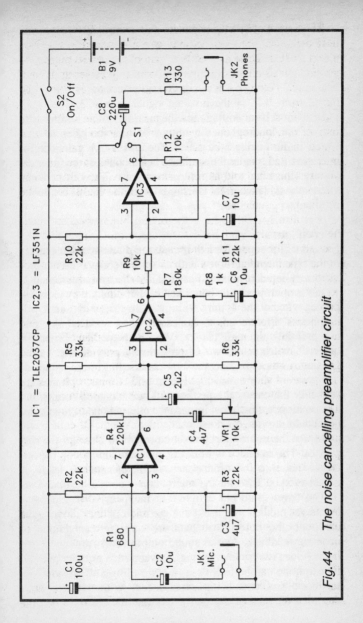

Fig.44   The noise cancelling preamplifier circuit

IC1 = TLE2037CP   IC2,3 = LF351N

113

The output of IC1 is coupled to gain control VR1, and from here the signal is fed to the input of a non-inverting amplifier based on IC2. This has a voltage gain of about 180 times. IC3 simply acts as a unity voltage gain inverting buffer at the output of IC2. Using S1 it is possible to select the non-inverted signal from IC2, or the inverted signal from IC3. The headphones are driven via R13, and the purpose of this resistor is to reduce the loading on the output of the amplifier so that higher audio quality is obtained. The unit is only intended for operation with medium impedance headphones of the inner ear variety (the type sold as replacements for use with personal stereo units). The current consumption of the circuit is about 6 milliamps per channel.

Microphones

I found that inexpensive low impedance dynamic microphones of the type intended for use with cassette recorders did not provide very good results. Higher quality dynamic microphones would probably provide better results, but I did not have an opportunity to try the system with more up-market dynamic microphones. Electret microphones provided good results, and are probably the best choice. Very high quality "broadcast quality" microphones would presumably provide the flattest frequency response, and the best results, but microphones of this type are very expensive. Electret tie-clip microphones are probably the cheapest type that will provide good results, but any omni-directional low impedance microphone of high quality should provide good results.

In use the microphones must be mounted close to the earphones. The easiest way of doing this is to simply clip the microphones onto the headphones, or the headphone leads. A neater method is to fix the microphones onto a headband removed from some old or new but inexpensive headphones. Whatever method you use, have the microphones close to the earphones, but not so close that there is a significant amount of acoustic feedback. As the sound output level from inner ear headphones is very low, the gap between each microphone and its earphone can be as little as a few millimetres without any feedback problems being experienced. With a microphone mounted on each of the user's ears there is clearly a definite advantage in using microphones that are very small, such as miniature tie-clip microphones. Make sure that the right hand microphone drives the right hand earphone, and that the microphones and earphones are not cross wired.

With everything in place and operating properly it is time to experiment a little with the gain controls and the phase switches in an attempt to get some noise cancelling. When experimenting with this type of equipment I find it helpful to use an f.m. radio tuned between stations to act as a noise source. The noise covers a wide frequency range, and it is a good test for noise cancelling equipment.

Results with the prototype equipment, once carefully set up, were reasonably good. With systems of this type it is usually possible to obtain good noise cancelling at lower and middle frequencies, but high frequencies seem to represent a major problem. This was certainly the case with the prototype equipment, which seems to produce about 20dB or so of attenuation over a fairly wide frequency range, but is not very good at high frequencies. There are several factors which could be causing problems at treble frequencies.

The obvious one is that the microphones and headphones are likely to roll-off high and low frequencies to some extent, producing a reduction in the level of noise cancelling. This lack of cancelling tends to be more obvious on high frequency sounds than on low frequency types. Another possible cause of problems at the upper end of the audio range is that of phase shifts. The high frequency phase shift through the amplifier is probably not very great, but there are almost certainly further high frequency phase lags through microphones and the headphones. It would presumably be possible to improve matters by using some high frequency boost plus some phase correction, but this could be quite difficult to get just right in practice. Anyway, it represents an interesting challenge for the experimenter, and an improved noise cancelling system is something that I will certainly be trying to perfect in due course.

Components for Noise Cancelling Preamplifier (Fig. 44)

Resistors (all 0.25 watt 5% carbon film)
R1	680R
R2	22k
R3	22k
R4	220k
R5	33k
R6	33k
R7	180k
R8	1k
R9	10k
R10	22k
R11	22k
R12	10k
R13	330R

Potentiometer
VR1	10k log carbon

Capacitors
C1	100µ 10V elect
C2	10µ 25V elect
C3	4µ7 50V elect
C4	4µ7 50V elect
C5	2µ2 50V elect
C6	10µ 25V elect
C7	10µ 25V elect
C8	220µ 10V elect

Semiconductors
IC1	TLE2037CP
IC2	LF351N
IC3	LF351N

Miscellaneous
JK1	6.35mm jack socket
JK2	3.5mm stereo jack socket
S1	SPDT min toggle
S2	SPST min toggle

B1   9 volt (6 × HP7 size cells in holder)
                Case
                Circuit board
                Control knob
                8 pin DIL IC holder (3 off)
                Battery connector (PP3 type)
                Low impedance microphone (see text)
                Medium impedance inner ear headphones
                Wire, solder, etc.

Note that apart from B1, S2, the battery connector, the headphones, and JK2, two of each component are needed in order to provide two channel operation.

CLASS D 555

Class D audio output stages are by no means a new idea, and I seem to remember some small but quite powerful Sinclair amplifier modules of this type that were available in the 1960s. I believe that Sony marketed a 2 × 160 watt Class D amplifier around 1980, but this class of amplification has never been in widespread use. A Class D output stage is really just a modified version of a conventional Class B type, and it is actually somewhat simpler. It is the circuitry that precedes the driver and output stage that is radically different, and a Class D amplifier is as much digital as analogue.

It is the digital nature of the output signal that brings definite advantages. The input stages generate a standard p.w.m. (pulse width modulation) signal at a typical frequency of about 200kHz. Under quiescent conditions the output signal is a squarewave having a 1 to 1 mark-space ratio. The average output voltage from the amplifier is therefore about half the supply voltage. If the input voltage is increased, the mark-space ratio of the output signal also increases, and produces a higher average output voltage. Figure 45 shows a varying input voltage and the type of p.w.m. output waveform that this would generate.

Simply feeding the p.w.m. output signal direct to a loudspeaker more or less guarantees a minor disaster. Even though the p.w.m. signal is at a fairly high frequency, with its

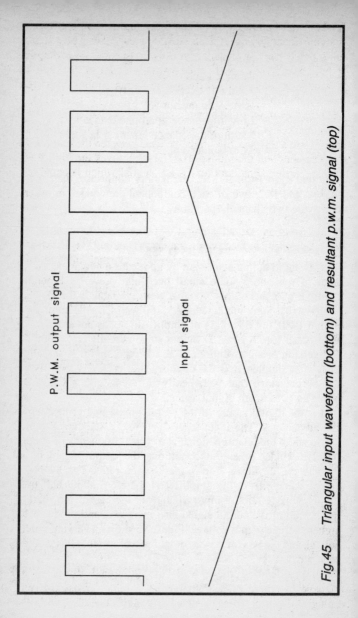

P.W.M. output signal

Input signal

Fig.45   Triangular input waveform (bottom) and resultant p.w.m. signal (top)

118

fundamental frequency about ten times higher than the upper limit of the audio range, the coil in the loudspeaker will still offer a fairly low impedance at this frequency. The output signal has a peak-to-peak value virtually equal to the supply voltage used, and would therefore be strong enough to drive very high currents through the loudspeaker. This could easily result in the output stage burning out, and could also have dire consequences for the loudspeaker. In order to obtain the desired result a lowpass filter must be used between the output of the amplifier and the loudspeaker. This removes the high frequency carrier signal and leaves a potential which is equal to the average voltage of the p.w.m. signal.

Advantages

So just what are the advantages of using Class D amplification? A problem with conventional Class B output stages is that of avoiding cross-over distortion. The normal method of combating this type of distortion is to use a moderate bias current through the output transistors under quiescent conditions, so that they are never in the "off" state. This in itself brings other problems, one of which is thermal instability. The quiescent bias current causes the output transistors to heat up slightly, which results in them conducting more heavily, which in turn results in an increased bias current. Unless some form of temperature stabilising circuit is included in the output stage, this regenerative action continues until the output transistors overheat and are destroyed.

The other main problem is that the bias current only reduces cross-over distortion, rather than completely eliminating it. The normal solution is to use large amounts of negative feedback to reduce the cross-over distortion to an insignificant level. This feedback also reduces any other distortion through the output and driver stages. Masses of negative feedback is very effective at reducing the distortion figure of a Class B amplifier, but it is a method that has by no means achieved universal approval.

The linearity of a Class D amplifier is largely governed by the quality of the p.w.m. circuit, and not the output stage. The output transistors operate as simple switches, and their linearity (or lack of it) is of no consequence. This makes it unnecessary to use a quiescent bias through the output transistors, cross-over distortion is completely eliminated, as is any risk of thermal runaway.

This is not to say that the driver and output stages can not introduce any distortion. These stages must have a fast switching time so that they do not distort the mark-space ratio of the input signal. Any smearing of the signal or other irregularities that are produced will generate distortion products on the audio output signal. Some of the power transistors of yesteryear were very slow, but most modern silicon power transistors have quite respectable bandwidths, and are well suited to operation in Class D output stages. It is possible to apply negative feedback over a Class D amplifier in order to reduce distortion, but there are practical difficulties. Most Class D amplifiers are designed to achieve an adequate level of distortion performance without resorting to any negative feedback over the driver and output stages.

One of the main advantages of Class D amplifiers is their relatively high efficiency. This is aided by the lack of any quiescent bias current through the output stage, which permits a very low current consumption to be achieved under standby conditions. However, even when operating at high volume levels a Class D amplifier can be relatively efficient. This is due to the fact that the output transistors operate as switches, and therefore dissipate relatively little power.

When an output transistor is switched off it has virtually the full supply voltage across its collector and emitter terminals, but the current flow is negligible (probably less than one microamp). The power dissipation in the device is therefore negligible. When an output transistor is switched on, it passes a high current, but the voltage across its collector and emitter terminals is quite low. Unfortunately, power devices do provide significant voltage drops when handling high currents, and a significant power is dissipated in each power transistor when it is switched on and the amplifier is delivering a high output current.

Although a practical Class D output stage can not achieve the 100% efficiency that is possible in theory, it is certainly possible to achieve an efficiency of more than 90%. This compares to an efficiency of about 60 to 70% for a reasonably efficient Class B circuit. It may not seem to be worthwhile striving for extra efficiency when an ordinary Class B output stage provides a respectable level of performance in this regard. On the other hand, it could still be worthwhile if a battery operated power amplifier is required. The greater efficiency of a Class D design, plus its very low quiescent current consumption, could practically double the battery life.

Also bear in mind that the power dissipated in the output transistors is converted into heat. Class B amplifiers having quite modest output powers often require large heatsinks for their output transistors. Even quite high powered Class D amplifiers often require nothing more than a small clip-on or bolt-on heatsink on each output transistor. This enables Class D amplifiers to be very much smaller than an equivalent Class B design.

Drawbacks

Class D amplifiers undoubtedly have their advantages, but they also have some major drawbacks. The most obvious of these is that the p.w.m. circuitry results in greater cost and complexity compared to an equivalent Class B design. Probably most designers would consider the problem of high frequency breakthrough at the output a more major drawback. In theory there is no difficulty in greatly attenuating the high frequency signals present in the p.w.m. output signal. In reality it is quite difficult to provide a high degree of attenuation because the filter must be a passive type. Furthermore, it must provide a low resistance path so that it provides minimal losses, and permits most of the output signal to reach the loudspeaker.

In practice the output filter is normally an L – C type, and a single stage filter provides an attenuation rate of 12dB per octave. In practice the presence of a low impedance loudspeaker at the output of the filter will tend to degrade the performance slightly, but it is still possible to obtain about 40dB of attenuation without seriously rolling off the upper frequency response of the amplifier. This would typically leave the p.w.m. signal at about 250 millivolts peak-to-peak in the loudspeaker lead. This is not acceptable if a long loudspeaker lead is used, as it would result in quite strong radio frequency interference being radiated. In order to obtain insignificant

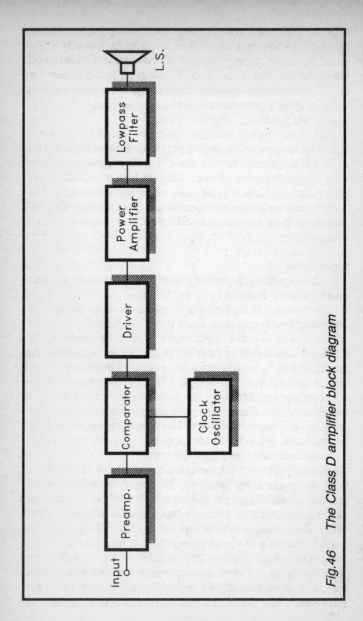

Fig.46   The Class D amplifier block diagram

radio frequency emissions with a long loudspeaker lead it is necessary to have about 80dB or more of attenuation at the p.w.m. clock frequency, and this requires a multi-stage L – C lowpass filter. Provided a short loudspeaker lead is used (i.e. the amplifier and loudspeaker are mounted in the same cabinet) about 40dB of attenuation should be satisfactory.

P.W.M.

The block diagram of Figure 46 shows the general make-up for a Class D amplifier. The driver and power amplifier stages are basically just the same as their equivalents in a standard Class B amplifier, and the lowpass filter stage was discussed previously. A preamplifier at the input simply gives the circuit the required input impedance and sensitivity. The clock oscillator and comparator stages form a conventional p.w.m. circuit. The oscillator is a triangular type, and it is essential for it to produce a high quality output signal. Any lack of linearity in its output waveform will be reflected in a similar lack of linearity from the amplifier as a whole.

The waveforms of Figure 47 help to explain the way in which the p.w.m. process operates. The top pair of waveforms show the clock signal and the output signal from the comparator under quiescent conditions. The output voltage from the preamplifier is half way between the maximum and minimum clock signal voltages. The output of the comparator goes high when the input voltage from the preamplifier is higher than the clock oscillator's output voltage. The comparator's output goes low when the signal from the preamplifier is the one at the lower potential. This gives the required squarewave output signal under standby conditions.

In the middle pair of waveforms the input level from the preamplifier has been increased. The input signal is now at a higher potential than the clock signal for a greater percentage of the time, giving an output signal from the comparator that has a higher mark-space ratio than previously. In the bottom pair of waveforms the input signal has been taken lower in voltage. Consequently, the input signal is at a higher voltage than the clock signal for only a small proportion of the time, giving an output signal having a low mark-space ratio. The mark-space ratio of the output signal, and the average voltage of this

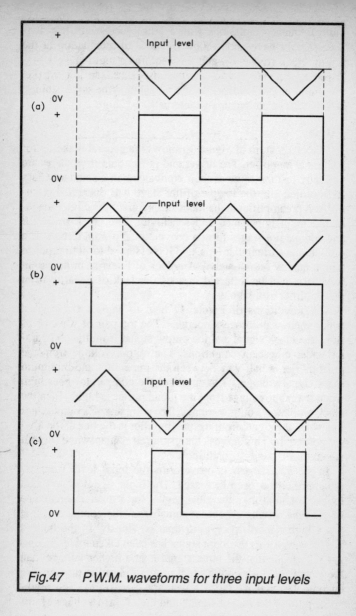

Fig.47   P.W.M. waveforms for three input levels

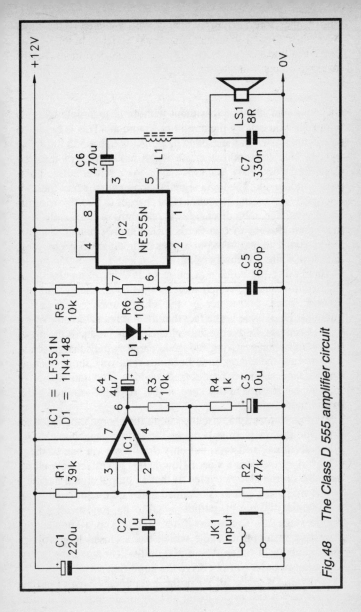

Fig.48   The Class D 555 amplifier circuit

signal, therefore vary in sympathy with changes in the input voltage. Provided the triangular clock signal is highly linear, there is a linear relationship between the input voltage and the average output voltage.

555 Circuit

If you would like to experiment with an ultra-simple Class D amplifier you can try the circuit of Figure 48. This is based on a 555 timer used in the astable mode. Although a 555 timer can not provide conventional pulse width modulation of the type described previously, it can act as a crude but effective pulse width modulator. The input signal is applied to pin 5 of the 555. Normally the timing capacitor (C5) charges to two-thirds of the supply voltage, then discharges to one-third of the supply voltage, then charges to two-thirds of the supply potential again, and so on. The output at pin 3 goes high while C5 is charging, and low while it is discharging.

Increasing the voltage at pin 5 of IC2 increases the upper threshold potential, which increases both the charge and discharge times, but increases the charge time by a greater amount. This is due to the fact that the normal symmetry of the circuit is upset. Reducing the voltage at pin 5 reduces the upper threshold voltage, giving reduced charge and discharge times. In this case the charge time becomes relatively short. Varying the voltage at pin 5 produces frequency modulation, but of greater importance in this case, it also gives the required pulse width modulation.

With a standard 555 astable circuit the charge time is longer than the discharge time because the timing capacitor charges via both timing resistors, but only discharges via one of them. This circuit includes a steering diode (D1) to effectively eliminate R6 during charge cycles so that an output signal having a 1 to 1 mark-space ratio is obtained under quiescent conditions. C6 couples the p.w.m. output signal to the loudspeaker via a single stage L – C lowpass filter. IC1 acts as a simple non-inverting preamplifier stage which has a closed loop voltage gain of about 11 times. About 300 millivolts r.m.s. is needed at the input in order to fully drive the amplifier.

No value is given for L1 in the components list as I did not obtain very good results using a ready-made inductor. A value of about 470µH is needed, but there were instability problems when I tried using ready-made inductors of around this value. Some of the inductors provided reasonable results when the circuit was used to drive a high impedance loudspeaker, but the output power was then rather limited. I found that the best results were produced using a home constructed inductor consisting of about 70 turns of 24 s.w.g. enamelled copper wire wound on a 4BA bolt. It will probably be necessary to experiment a little with the number of turns on the inductor. With too few turns the circuit will probably work, but with a rather high quiescent current consumption. With too many turns there will be a noticeable lack of high frequency response, and probably a lack of output power as well.

This circuit does not represent a particularly serious attempt at a Class D amplifier, but it is an interesting novelty circuit that can be made to work if a suitable inductor is used. The output power is not very great, but the maximum volume obtained is more than adequate for many practical applications. The audio quality is not hi-fi, but it is surprisingly good under the circumstances. Remember that the linearity of the output stage is not aided by the use of any negative feedback.

Components for 555 Class D Amplifier (Fig. 48)

Resistors (all 0.25 watt 5% carbon film)

R1	39k
R2	47k
R3	10k
R4	1k
R5	10k
R6	10k

Capacitors

C1	220µ 16V elect
C2	1µ 50V elect
C3	10µ 25V elect
C4	4µ7 50V elect
C5	680p polystyrene
C6	470µ 16V elect
C7	330n polyester

127

Semiconductors
IC1   LF351N
IC2   NE555N
D1   1N4148

Miscellaneous
L1   See text
LS1   8R miniature moving coil loudspeaker
JK1   3.5mm jack socket
                Case
                Circuit board
                8 pin DIL IC holder (2 off)
                Wire, solder, etc.

REAL CLASS D

Figures 49 to 51 show the circuit diagram for a "real" Class D amplifier of conventional design. Figure 49 shows the circuit for the pulse width modulator. The triangular clock signal is generated by an oscillator of the type that has one operational amplifier (IC1a) as an integrator and another (IC1b) as a trigger circuit. This configuration gives a squarewave signal at the output of the trigger circuit, and a triangular output signal from the integrator. In this case it is only the triangular output signal from IC1a that is required. The operating frequency of the oscillator is set at about 180kHz by timing components C2 and R3. IC2 is the voltage comparator.

Although this part of the circuit may seem to be perfectly straightforward, it is rather problematic. Getting a pulse width modulator to work well at a frequency of a few kilohertz or less is one thing – satisfactory operation at nearly 200kHz is quite another. It is important that the dual operational amplifier used in the IC1 position has a wide bandwidth and a high slew rate. The operating speed of IC1 may not seem to be of great importance, since its triangular output signal varies at a relatively low rate. The point that has to be borne in mind is that the triangular signal is effectively derived from the squarewave output signal from IC1b. Any deficiencies in this squarewave signal will produce a lack of linearity in the triangular output signal.

128

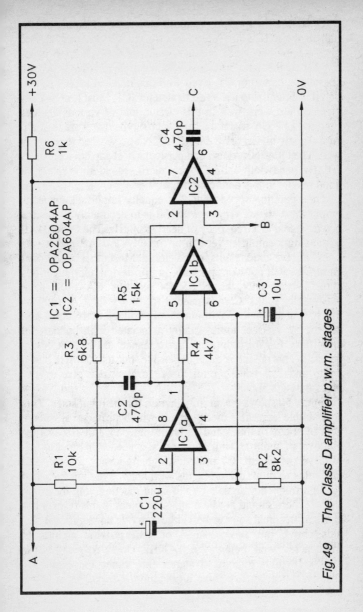

Fig.49   The Class D amplifier p.w.m. stages

129

Operating the modulator circuit on a reduced supply potential of about 12 volts seems to ease the burden on IC1, and gives a better triangular output signal. The 12 volt supply is derived from the main 30 volt supply via dropper resistor R6 and smoothing capacitor C1. Even with this reduced supply potential, it is essential to use a fast device for IC1. Most low cost devices do not work well in this circuit, and of various devices tried the LF353N was the only low cost type that worked at all. At a slightly higher price the NE5532N also worked reasonably well. The OPA2604AP is not a particularly cheap device, but its 20MHz bandwidth and 25V per micro-second slew rate give good results in this application.

The operating speed of IC2 is equally important, since its output must switch very rapidly if it is to accurately produce a p.w.m. signal at a frequency of nearly 200kHz. The OPA604AP is the single amplifier version of the OPA2604AP, and it was found to give good results in this circuit. Most other operational amplifiers will not work properly in this design. Of the various chips I tried only the NE5534N and the CA3130E gave reasonable results. Care is needed if you try the CA3130E as this has an absolute maximum supply voltage of 16 volts, and not the 36 volts or more usually associated with operational amplifiers. For the ultimate in performance an EL2045CN can be used. This device is quite expensive, but its 100MHz bandwidth and 275 volts per microsecond slew rate give a very precise output signal.

Figure 50 shows the circuit diagram for the input stage. This is a simple inverting mode circuit which provides a voltage gain of about 10 times and an input impedance of 10k. An input level of about 150 millivolts r.m.s. is needed in order to fully drive the circuit. C7 provides high frequency roll-off, and this helps to minimise problems with heterodyne tones caused by high frequency signals on the input reacting with the clock signal. There should not be a major problem in this respect because most signal sources will either provide no significant signals above the audio range, or will provide signals at frequencies well below the 180kHz clock frequency (the 19/38kHz pilot tone of a stereo f.m. tuner for example). However, if necessary some more comprehensive input filtering must be added.

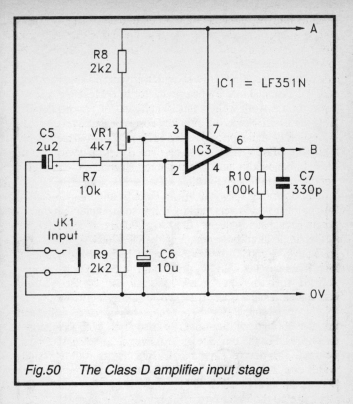

Fig.50   The Class D amplifier input stage

The circuit diagram for the driver, output, and filter stages appears in Figure 51. The p.w.m. signal from IC2 is coupled to the base of TR1 which operates as a simple common emitter switch. This stage is the equivalent of the driver stage in a conventional Class B amplifier. TR1 drives a complementary output stage which consists of two pairs of common emitter amplifiers. Although common emitter stages normally have high voltage gains, in this case there is 100% negative feedback from the collector of the second transistor to the emitter of the first transistor. This gives only unity voltage gain, and the pairs of output transistors operate as high gain buffer stages. C8 provides d.c. blocking at the output, and the lowpass filtering is provided by L1 and C9. This filter leaves about 250 millivolts

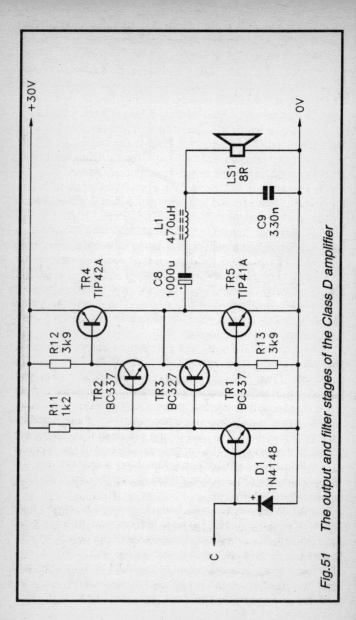

Fig.51   The output and filter stages of the Class D amplifier

of clock ripple on the output signal. The amplifier should therefore only be used with a short loudspeaker lead unless a higher quality filter is used at the output.

Although output transistors TR4 and TR5 operate as switches and dissipate relatively little power, it is still necessary to fit them with at least small bolt-on or clip-on heatsinks. I used a clip-on type rated at 13.6 degrees Celsius per watt. Inductor L1 must be a type which will operate properly at frequencies of up to a few hundred kilohertz, and it must also be able to handle currents of several hundred milliamps. Its resistance must be as low as possible so that it introduces minimal losses.

The best type of inductor for this application seems to be one wound on a pot-core, and intended for use in high power switch mode power supplies. The RS/Electromail "High Current Radial" inductor "type B" is just about ideal, with its resistance of just 129 milliohms and current rating of 4 amps. The "type A" inductor is somewhat cheaper though, and has ratings that are more than adequate (244 milliohms and 2.3 amps). The Maplin 470µH "Bobbin Type Inductor" seems to be identical, and works equally well in this circuit. The other inductors I tried, including some home-wound components, did not work particularly well in this design.

The circuit should work using alternative output transistors, but some power devices do not work well in the TR4 and TR5 positions. Presumably due to a slightly inadequate switching speed, these devices produce a relatively high quiescent current flow that steadily increases, giving a sort of thermal runaway effect. If you use alternative output transistors, check that they are free from this effect, and do not use them if there are any signs of this problem. The current consumption of the circuit is not particularly high by power amplifier standards, but the supply should be reasonably stable and capable of delivering at least 500 milliamps.

This circuit involves both fairly high frequencies and high currents. The component layout is fairly critical with any power amplifier, but is even more important with a power amplifier of this type. Use a layout that avoids any obvious stray feedback paths from the output of the input of the circuit, and pay careful attention to the earthing arrangements.

Results

Initially VR1 should be set at a roughly central position. If an oscilloscope is available, adjust VR1 so that under standby conditions the signal at pin 3 of IC2 has a 1 to 1 mark-space ratio. If you do not have access to an oscilloscope, use an analogue multimeter to monitor the voltage at the positive terminal of C8, and then adjust VR1 for a reading of 15 volts. Alternatively, simply adjust VR1 for the setting that enables the highest volume to be obtained without the amplifier clipping and producing severe distortion.

Results from the amplifier were quite encouraging, but the maximum peak-to-peak output voltage was rather less than I expected. The output voltage swing obtained was several volts less than the supply potential, giving a maximum output power of a little over 8 watts r.m.s. Considering the lack of any overall negative feedback the audio quality is quite good, but is not really in the hi-fi category. The circuit is good enough for medium-fi applications though.

I tried the alternative output stages of Figures 52 and 53. In the circuit of Figure 52 the pairs of common emitter amplifiers have been replaced with power Darlington devices. Although Darlington amplifiers tend to be regarded as very slow, the TIP122, TIP127, and similar devices have quite respectable switching speeds, and the power Darlington output stage worked reasonably well. It was a little inconsistent though, with some devices seeming to work rather better than others. The maximum output power seemed to be slightly less than that provided by the common emitter output stage, but the audio quality seemed to be much the same.

Power MOSFETs would seem to be well suited to Class D amplification as they have quite fast switching times for such high power transistors. I used a 2SK133/2SJ48 complementary pair, but results would probably be much the same using any other matched complementary power MOSFETs. The output stage of Figure 53 certainly did not lack in switching speed, but it did not work particularly well either! One problem is that power MOSFETs tend to introduce relatively high voltage drops, giving a relatively low output power for a given supply voltage. Provided you are prepared to tolerate this reduced efficiency, using a higher supply voltage to the output and

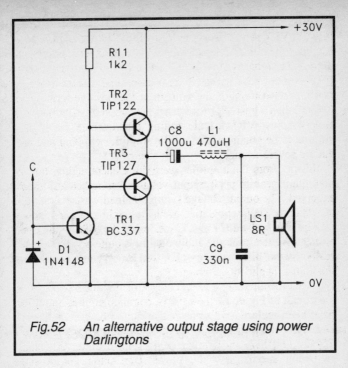

Fig.52   An alternative output stage using power Darlingtons

driver stages would restore the maximum output power to the level offered by the common emitter output stage.

Unfortunately, this still leaves a problem with instability. I am not quite sure what caused this, but instability seems to produce a very rough sounding output signal on output powers of more than a watt or two. Results were actually better with C4, D1, TR1, and R11 omitted, and the gate terminals of TR2 and TR3 driven from the output (pin 6) of IC2. There still seemed to be an instability problem though, and the efficiency of the amplifier was reduced still further. Considering the relatively high cost of power MOSFETs, fast bipolar power transistors would seem to be a much better choice for this application.

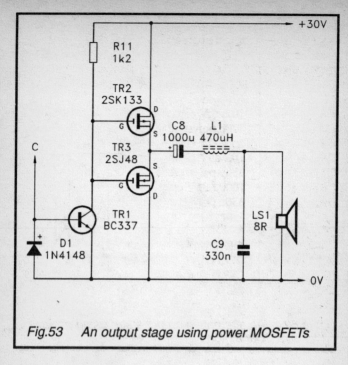

Fig.53   An output stage using power MOSFETs

Components for Class D Amplifier (Figs 49, 50, and 51)

Resistors (all 0.25 watt 5% carbon film unless note)

R1	10k
R2	8k2
R3	6k8
R4	4k7
R5	15k
R6	1k 1 watt
R7	10k
R8	2k2
R9	2k2
R10	100k
R11	1k2
R12	3k9
R13	3k9

Potentiometer

VR1   4k7 min preset

Capacitors

C1	220µ 40V elect
C2	470p polystyrene
C3	10µ 50V elect
C4	470p polystyrene
C5	2µ2 50V elect
C6	10µ 25V elect
C7	330p polystyrene
C8	1000µ 25V elect
C9	330n polyester

Semiconductors

IC1	OPA2604AP
IC2	OPA604AP
IC3	LF351N
TR1	BC337
TR2	BC337
TR3	BC327
TR4	TIP42A
TR5	TIP41A
D1	1N4148

Miscellaneous

JK1	Standard 6.35mm jack socket
LS1	8 ohm impedance, rated at 10 watts r.m.s. or more
L1	470µH (see text)
	Case
	Circuit board
	Two clip-on TO220 heat sinks
	8 pin DIL IC holder (3 off)
	Wire, solder, etc.